INORGANIC COMPLEX COMPOUNDS

Selected Topics in Modern Chemistry

SERIES EDITORS

Professor Harry H. Sisler
University of Florida
Gainesville, Florida

Professor Calvin A. VanderWerf
Hope College
Holland, Michigan

CHELDELIN AND NEWBURGH—*The Chemistry of Some Life Processes*
EYRING AND EYRING—*Modern Chemical Kinetics*
HILDEBRAND—*An Introduction to Molecular Kinetic Theory*
KIEFFER—*The Mole Concept in Chemistry*
MOELLER—*The Chemistry of the Lanthanides*
MURMANN—*Inorganic Complex Compounds*
O'DRISCOLL—*The Nature and Chemistry of High Polymers*
OVERMAN—*Basic Concepts of Nuclear Chemistry*
ROCHOW—*Organometallic Chemistry*
RYSCHKEWITSCH—*Chemical Bonding and the Geometry of Molecules*
SISLER—*Chemistry in Non-Aqueous Solvents*
SISLER—*Electronic Structure, Properties, and the Periodic Law*
VANDERWERF—*Acids, Bases, and the Chemistry of the Covalent Bond*
VOLD AND VOLD—*Colloid Chemistry*

Series Editors' Statement

THE STUDY of the complexes of metal ions has challenged both the synthetic and theoretical capabilities of several generations of inorganic and physical chemists. As a result, new ideas, new experimental techniques, and new theoretical concepts have originated in profusion from research in this area. It is, therefore, most appropriate that complex ion chemistry should be represented by a volume in our SELECTED TOPICS IN MODERN CHEMISTRY SERIES. We are pleased that Professor Murmann, whose contributions to research and instruction in complex ion chemistry are so well known, has consented to prepare this stimulating volume.

HARRY H. SISLER
CALVIN A. VANDERWERF

INORGANIC
COMPLEX COMPOUNDS

R. KENT MURMANN

Professor of Chemistry
University of Missouri
Columbia, Missouri

New York
REINHOLD PUBLISHING CORPORATION
Chapman & Hall Ltd., London

PREFACE

In writing this book I have attempted to present to undergraduate chemistry students and to students in neighboring fields some of the basic concepts involved in the formation of metal complexes. A selection of topics has been made partly on the basis of the success of lectures in General Chemistry and Inorganic Chemistry as judged by examinations. Several important areas have been only mentioned in passing. In these cases I felt that a short treatment would hinder rather than help the student.

This book describes some of the experimental methods used in studies of the properties of complex ions, shows some selected experimental results and the resulting theories, and presents some areas where the author expects important advances in the future. Written for the student who wishes to know what can be and what has been done with these colorful compounds, the book is short enough to be read in one sitting. Then, if it is successful as a learning-teaching tool, it will continue to be studied and to provide the student with increasing insight into coordination chemistry throughout his undergraduate training.

The author would like to express his gratitude to his graduate students for their helpful suggestions, to Mrs. Letcher, Dr. J. Beard, and Mrs. Belfer who assisted in the preparation of the manuscript, and to his wife and children for their patience.

Columbia, Missouri
November, 1964

R. Kent Murmann

CONTENTS

Preface   vii

1. Introduction to Coordination Chemistry   1

2. Thermodynamic Stability of Complex Compounds   25

3. Reaction Speeds of Complex Species   54

4. Modes of Bonding   66

5. Properties and Characteristic Reactions   82

6. Application of Coordination Theory   110

Selected Readings   118

Index   119

INTRODUCTION

HISTORICALLY, few branches of chemistry have received as much concentrated study with such fruitful results as the area encompassed by coordination chemistry. This science is now in a state of rapid advance similar to that experienced by organic chemistry nearly 100 years ago. This is shown by the fact that many of the ideas and theories of 20 years ago have already been either discarded or modified. It is to be expected that future progress will be even more rapid, and thus, for beginning as well as established scientists, coordination chemistry will be an extremely attractive field of research.

One of the earliest recorded coordination compounds is prussian blue, an artist's color, made by accident when animal wastes and Na_2CO_3 were strongly heated in an iron container. Other long-known compounds are potassium ferrocyanide (1753), K_2PtCl_6 (1760–65), and $[Co(NH_3)_6]Cl_3$ (1798).

The first era of rapid activity in this field began in 1798 when Tassaert isolated orange crystals of $CoCl_3 \cdot 6NH_3$ by allowing a mixture of $CoCl_2$ and aqueous ammonia to stand in air. He puzzled over the fact that two stable compounds would combine to form a new product with properties entirely different from the compounds it contained. Numerous compounds of this type were prepared in the following century, including those containing other metals such as iron and platinum. During this time many theories were proposed to explain the attraction between two compounds capable of independent existence and attempts were made to deduce the structure of these "complex" compounds. However, the theories suggested followed the prevailing views in organic chemistry, and important progress was impeded.

In 1877 Arrhenius proposed the concept of ionization, and the climate again became favorable for development of useful theoretical concepts. It was Alfred Werner who began the second phase of rapid advance in this field with the theory of "primary" and "secondary" valences. He suggested that "primary" valences were those satisfying the normal charge on the ion and that the "secondary" valences were those used in attaching the coordinating groups (e.g., ammonia molecules). Further he showed that the factor determining the chemical properties of coordination compounds was not the "primary" valence, but the number of "secondary" valences which the metal ion possessed. Thus a complex containing more groups than the number of secondary valences (the coordination number) would have the excess outside the direct influence of the metal and these groups would be present as ions associated through electrostatic forces.

In the early days many complexes were named according to the complex color. This is illustrated in Table 1-1. According to Werner's theory the luteo salt contains six "secondary valences" holding the ammonia molecules to the metal, while the three chlorine atoms are ionically bound through three "primary valences." In the purpureo complex the coordination sphere ("secondary valence") is completed

TABLE 1-1. Early Nomenclature

Composition	Formula	Color	Name
$CoCl_3 \cdot 6\,NH_3$	$[Co(NH_3)_6]Cl_3$	Yellow	Luteocobaltic chloride
$CoCl_3 \cdot 5\,NH_3$	$[Co(NH_3)_5Cl]Cl_2$	Purple	Purpureocobaltic chloride
$CoCl_3 \cdot 4\,NH_3$	*trans*-$[Co(NH_3)_4Cl_2]Cl$	Green	Praseocobaltic chloride

by five ammonia molecules and a chlorine atom, leaving two atoms of chlorine ionically bound. This suggested that one of the chlorines was different from the other two, and indeed cold silver nitrate solution precipitates only two-thirds of the chlorine.

Important advancements were made during the years 1891–1915, but the pace slowed while theoretical and physical chemical ideas were being developed. The important contributions of G. N. Lewis (1916) to the theories of bonding were extended and applied to coordination chemistry by N. V. Sidgwick (1927).

In 1939 the stage was set for renewed activity in this field prompted by the availability of physical chemical methods and instruments and by the valence bond theory developed by Linus Pauling. The results of work done in the last 20 years have been substantial advances in the areas of kinetic and thermodynamic stability, mechanisms of reaction, stereochemistry, oxidation-reduction, synthesis, and theories of bonding, to name a few.

Definition of a Coordination Compound

Chemists are not completely agreed on a simple universal definition of a coordination compound. Since the thermodynamic stabilities as well as the rates of reaction vary over extremely wide limits, it is difficult to offer a definition which is applicable to all cases.

According to the theory of Sidgwick and Lowry, a coordinate bond consists of the union of an atom, molecule, or ion which can accept a pair of electrons from another atom, molecule, or ion which is able to donate a pair of electrons. The result is a pair of electrons shared between two atoms, molecules, or ions. In metal coordination compounds a metal ion is the electron pair acceptor and usually is able to accept more than one pair. The number of electron pairs which can be used in bonding is called the coordination number (C.N.), known values of which are 2, 3, 4, 5, 6, 8. The donor atom is usually nonmetallic and is often part of a molecule capable of independent existence. This may be neutral, a negative ion or, occasionally, a positive ion. The donor molecule or ion is called the ligand, examples of which are NH_3, H_2O, CO, Cl^-, $(NO_3)^-$, $(N_2H_5)^+$. The resulting complex may be either a positive or negative ion or a neutral molecule depending on the balance of the metal and ligand ionic charges.

If we accept this definition of a coordinate bond, and thus of a coordination compound, the problem becomes one of deciding whether coordinate bonds are contained in individual compounds. This is a difficult task and usually the position is taken that bonds between species which can exist separately and which persist in solution are of the coordinate type. The presence of complex ions in solution can usually be demonstrated by a difference in chemical and/or physical properties between the complex and its component parts. In the solid state their existence may be revealed by crystal structure investigations using X-rays or neutron diffraction. It is not generally permissible to infer complex formation or establish the identity of the complex ions from the analytical composition, for many double salts and lattice compounds have in the past been erroneously suggested as coordination complexes.

We will be primarily concerned with complexes which retain their identity in solution and thus a useful definition of a metal coordination compound will be: *A compound formed between a metal ion and ligands, each capable of existing independently, through electron pair sharing using electrons from the ligands.* Further, the association will produce observable changes in the chemistry of both the metal ion and ligand.

It should be pointed out that although most ligands have an unshared pair of electrons for bonding, some very interesting and important classes of compounds contain ligands which do not appear to donate lone pairs of electrons. Such ligands as ethylene, aromatic hydrocarbons, carbon monoxide, and cyanide ion bond through the use of π-type orbitals, and the resultant bond has somewhat different properties.

General Nature and Uses of Complexes

Since most metal ions are coordinated to some extent in nearly any environment, the majority of inorganic reactions involving metal ions are directly concerned with coordination chemistry. An understanding of the mechanisms of even "simple" inorganic reactions requires at the minimum a quantitative knowledge about the constitution and environment of the reactants and products. One major aspect of coordination chemistry is the study of the interaction of metal ions with their environment, but as is often true in science, the "simple" systems may be the ones which are the most difficult to describe quantitatively. A comparison of a "simple" organic with a "simple" inorganic reaction will point out some of the problems found in inorganic systems.

In the hydrolysis of an ester (1-1) the molecular struc-

$$CH_3\overset{\overset{\displaystyle O}{\|}}{C}-OCH_3 + H_2O \rightleftharpoons CH_3\overset{\overset{\displaystyle O}{\|}}{C}-OH + CH_3OH \quad (1\text{-}1)$$

ture, bond angles, and interatomic distances are known for both reactants and products. Equally important is the fact that only weak association between the molecules exists because the species are essentially saturated molecules. Thus the experimenter may concentrate on reactive intermediates and on the mechanism involved. Contrast this with the problem of studying a "simple" inorganic reaction (1-2).

$$2\,Ce^{+4} + Sn^{+2} \rightleftharpoons 2\,Ce^{+3} + Sn^{+4} \quad (1\text{-}2)$$

It is well known that these bare ions do not exist in aqueous solution, but are extensively aquated; the number of water molecules associated in the first sphere is not known. Hydrolysis also occurs, but the exact nature of the hydrolysis products is uncertain. Further, negative ions must be present, and these replace coordinated solvent molecules, but the quantitative association constants are only now being measured. Concerning ourselves with only the Ce^{+4} as the chloride and assuming equilibrium is rapidly established, the following species will be present $[Ce(H_2O)_x]^{+4}$, $[Ce(H_2O)_xCl]^{+3}$, $[Ce(H_2O)_xCl_2]^{+2}$, $[Ce(H_2O)_x(OH)]^{+3}$, and some dimers and polymers having OH and Cl bridges. An equally large number of possibilities result with the other ions and since each molecule ion may have its own mode and rate of reaction, studies of the mechanism and demonstration of intermediates are completely dependent on a knowledge of the structures and coordinating tendencies of the metal ions. Another aspect of importance is the speed at which equilibrium is reached. Many simple associations with certain metal ions are extremely slow, such as reaction 1-3. A knowledge of the reaction kinetics of an ion is necessary before studies on other systems using these ions can be interpreted.

$$[Cr(H_2O)_6]^{+3} \;+\; Cl^- \;\rightleftharpoons\; [Cr(H_2O)_5Cl]^{+2} \;+\; H_2O \quad (1\text{-}3)$$

In analytical chemistry, aside from the usual quantitative reactions which involve the same type of complex species as described above, increasing use is being made of organic precipitating and complexing agents. A well-known example is 8-hydroxyquinoline (oxime), which selectively precipitates many metal ions through its coordinating ability. An organic chelating reagent which is extremely selective for Ni^{II} and Pd^{II} is dimethylglyoxime. It is extremely sensitive as well as selective and can be used in volumetric or gravimetric procedures. In recent years, ethylenediaminetetraacetic acid (EDTA) has simplified many metal ion determinations because of the thermodynamic stability of its metal complexes. Many other methods of analysis based on complex formation are in wide use including spectrophotometric methods, for example, determination of Fe^{II} as $[Fe(o\text{-phen})_3]^{+2}$,* which are well suited to coordination compounds because of the high molar absorbancies; ion exchange separations; polarographic determinations; and, recently, quantitative determination using the rate of formation or decomposition. This does not exhaust the list of techniques employing metal complexes but serves to demonstrate the need to investigate the underlying factors governing complex formation in order to design more sensitive reagents for metal ions which are also extremely selective.

The organic chemist often uses coordination compounds in preparative reactions, although he may not always recognize them as such. The Friedel-Crafts reaction employs metal chlorides (Al_2Cl_6, Fe_2Cl_6, etc.) in many alkylation reactions, the metal chloride complex behaving primarily as a Lewis acid. Other familiar examples are the Grignard reactions using RMgX and the Sandmeyer reaction which employs cuprous halides and no doubt involves complexation of the metal ion. In the area of catalysis, metal complexes are employed in the polymerization of ethylene (Ziegler type catalysts, Ti^{III} alkyls), and in homogeneous hydrogenation of olefins using $(i\text{-}C_4H_9)_3Al$ and $Co(acac)_3$. Numerous other applications have been made, some of which will be discussed in later chapters.

In physical chemistry, complexes have provided suitable compounds for testing and expanding the theories in the areas of bonding, electrolytic behavior of ions, magnetic behavior, solution thermodynamics, and theories of kinetic behavior, to name a few.

In recent years biochemists have become intensely interested in the effect of metal ions in the form of complexes on biological processes. Hemin and chlorophyll-a (Figs. 1-1 and

*For the definition of unfamiliar symbols see Table 1-3 on page 16.

1-2) contain coordinated Fe^{II} and Mg^{II}, respectively, while vitamin B_{12} contains cobalt ion at its center. Many enzymes are active only if trace amounts of metal ions are present and in many cases the active site of the enzyme is at a coordination position of the metal.

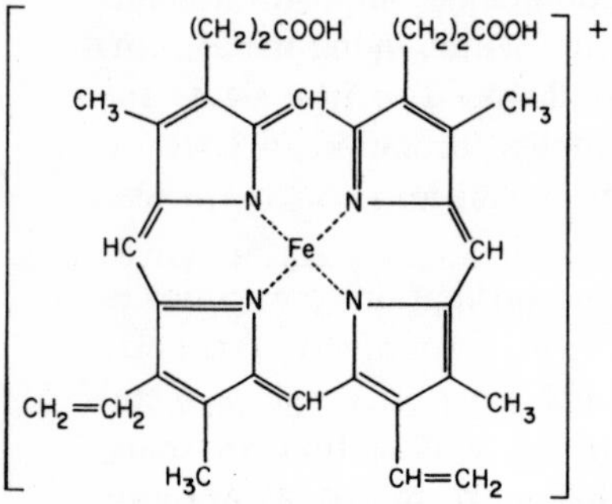

Figure 1-1. Hemin.

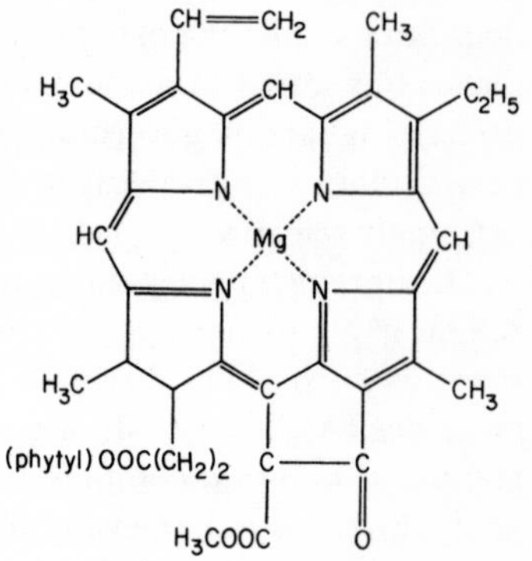

Figure 1-2. Chlorophyll-a.

Methods of Discerning Complex Formation

In general, any property of a system which is related to the concentration of one of the species involved in the formation of the complex (H^+, metal ion, ligand, or the complex) may be used to show the formation of a complex. Some other techniques which have been used are oxidation-reduction potentials, kinetic rate expressions, polarography, electrochemical migration, isotopic metal or ligand exchange, magnetic susceptibility, heats of mixing, volume changes, molar refraction, infrared absorption spectra, and nuclear magnetic resonance spectra. Since it is impossible to discuss here all of the methods which have been used, a selection has been made to include those of the greatest applicability.

Preparation. Historically, the first recognition of complex formation was through the preparation of solid substances having chemical and physical properties which differed from those of the starting materials. Just as in other branches of chemistry, the isolation and analysis of pure crystalline compounds constitute a widely used method of proving the existence of complexes. The isolation of yellow crystalline $K_3[Co(NO_2)_6]$ from the reaction of pink-colored $[Co(H_2O)_6]$-$(NO_3)_2$ with colorless KNO_2 proved that a complex between Co^{III} and NO_2^- exists and suggested that the coordination number is six. Moreover, an aqueous solution of $K_3[Co(NO_2)_6]$ gives none of the characteristic reactions of Co^{III} (such as precipitation with OH^- or S^-) or of NO_2^- (such as reaction with acid); rather, it behaves like a potassium salt (that is, precipitates with sodium tetraphenylboron, $Na(C_6H_5)_4B$), thus suggesting that ionization to $3K^+$ and $[Co(NO_2)_6]^{-3}$ occurs.

It is not always possible to infer solely from the formula of the solid compound the ions which exist in it or the ions which will be produced in aqueous solution. For example, Cs_3CoCl_5 has been isolated but does not contain $CoCl_5^{-3}$ The crystal structure as determined by X-ray diffraction shows the presence in the crystal of $[CoCl_4]^{-2}$, Cl^-, and Cs^+, and the compound should be regarded as a mixed crystal (lattice compound) of $CsCl$ and $Cs_2[CoCl_4]$.

Change in Chemical Properties. An important method for establishing that complexation occurs depends on the loss of the normal chemical properties of the metal ion in solution. The experimental fact that metal ions do not exhibit their usual reactions is positive evidence that the simple aquated ion is present in an extremely low concentration and thus that most of the metal ion is associated with ligands in the form of a complex. For example, $Fe(OH)_2$ does not precipitate upon the addition of OH^- to a solution of Fe^{II} in the presence of ethylenediaminetetraacetic acid (EDTA) because the iron is primarily in the form $[Fe(EDTA)]^{-2}$ and the concentration of free Fe^{II} is too small to exceed the solubility product. Similarly, Cl^- does not cause precipitation of Ag^+ from aqueous NH_3 solutions because of the stability of

$[Ag(NH_3)_2]^+$, whereas AgI, having a smaller solubility product, is easily precipitated. It should be pointed out, however, that complexes of low thermodynamic stability usually cannot be demonstrated by this technique owing to the appreciable amount of simple metal ion left uncomplexed. Thus complexes between NH_3 or alkylamines and Ca^{+2}, Zn^{+2}, or Al^{+3} give all of the usual precipitation reactions of the free metal ion.

Often the kinetics of reaction are more important than the complex formation constant. The complex formed between Cu^{II} and ammonia, $[Cu(NH_3)_4]^{+2}$, gives all of the usual sensitive tests for NH_3, including the formation of NH_4^+ with acids. $[Cr(NH_3)_6]^{+3}$ and $[Co(NH_3)_6]^{+3}$, however, show no reaction with H^+ or Nessler's reagent over a short period of time even at elevated temperatures. The difference is primarily, though not completely, due to the slow rate at which equilibrium is established with the latter two complexes.

Conductivity. The conductivity of solutions of complexes is often used to estimate the charge type. Except for complexes which ionize and give H^+_{aq} or OH^- upon solution, the molar conductivities at infinite dilution for many ion types have approximately the values in Table 1-2 at 25°C. One may determine the charge type by measuring the conductivity at infinite dilution provided that no appreciable decomposition or dissociation takes place before or during the time of measurement. Some metal ions which often exhibit kinetic stability are Pt^{IV}, Pt^{II}, Pd^{II}, Co^{III}, and Cr^{III}. As an example, a species of formula $Co(NH_3)_4(H_2O)_2Br_3$ shows an

TABLE 1-2. Infinite Dilution Molar Conductivity

Charge type	Ω^{-1}	Charge type
Complex^{+4}—4X$^-$	550	4M$^+$—complex^{-4}
Complex^{+3}—3X$^-$	430	3M$^+$—complex^{-3}
Complex^{+2}—2X$^-$	250	2M$^+$—complex^{-2}
Complex^{+1}—X$^-$	100	M$^+$—complex^{-1}
Complex^0	0	

infinite dilution molar conductivity of 420 suggesting a 3:1 charge type. On this basis its formulation is $[Co(NH_3)_4(H_2O)_2]Br_3$ rather than $[Co(NH_3)_4Br_2]Br \cdot 2H_2O$ or $[Co(NH_3)_4(H_2O)Br]Br_2 \cdot H_2O$.

In favorable situations conductivity is useful in establishing complex formation. The addition of two moles of glycine, NH_2CH_2COOH, to one mole of aqueous copper acetate solution decreases the solution conductivity because of the formation of a nonionic chelated complex (1-4). Because acetic acid is a weak acid, it contributes little to the conductivity.

$$[Cu(H_2O)_x]^{+2} + 2\ CH_3\overset{O}{\overset{\|}{C}}-O^- + 2\ NH_2CH_2COOH \longrightarrow$$

$$\left[\begin{array}{c} O=C-O \\ H_2C-N \end{array} \underset{Cu}{\overset{N^{H_2}CH_2}{\diagdown}} \begin{array}{c} N^{H_2}CH_2 \\ O-C=O \end{array} \right]^0 + 2\,CH_3COOH \quad (1-4)$$

The association of boric acid with α-glycols liberates H^+_{aq} and, owing to the hydrogen ion's high mobility, raises the conductivity (1-5). Since boric acid is a weak electrolyte

$$\begin{array}{c} R-C-OH \\ | \\ R-C-OH \end{array} + B(OH)_3 \rightleftharpoons$$

$$\begin{array}{c} R-C-O \\ | \\ R-C-O \end{array} \overset{O-C-R^-}{\underset{O-C-R}{\diagdown B \diagup}} \begin{array}{c} O-C-R^- \\ | \\ O-C-R \end{array} + H^+_{aq} + 3H_2O \quad (1-5)$$

and the complex is rather stable, the extent of coordination may be directly determined by measuring conductivity.

Visible and Ultraviolet Absorption. The absorption of light in the visible region (390–750 mμ) by a metal ion is dependent on the d-electron transitions within the ion and these are related to, among other things, the type and strength of ligand-to-metal bonding. Thus for metal ions containing d electrons (except those with $10d$ electrons), variable colors are observed depending on the ligands attached. Although most visible bands are not sharp, large frequency changes are usually observed, often allowing quick and definite conclusions to be made about complex formation. In many cases the intensities of absorption are increased when coordinated water is replaced by more basic ligands such as NH_3 (1-6) or ethylenediamine (1-7). The extent to which a

$$[Cu(H_2O)_4]^{+2} + 2\,en \rightleftharpoons [Cu(en)_2]^{+2} + 4\,H_2O \qquad (1\text{-}6)$$

Light blue   Deep purplish blue

$$[Cr(H_2O)_6]^{+3} + Cl^- \rightleftharpoons [Cr(H_2O)_5Cl]^{+2} + H_2O \qquad (1\text{-}7)$$

Violet   Green

spectrum can change is illustrated by Figure 1-3 where $[Ni(H_2O)_6]^{+2}$ is compared with an α-amineoxime complex. The absorption has shifted to higher energies (lower mμ) and has become more intense. Visible spectra measurements are well suited to quantitative equilibrium studies and to the

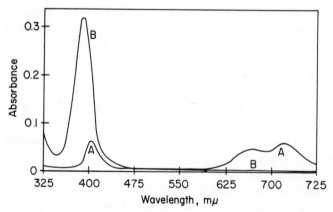

Figure 1-3. Visible Spectra of $[Ni(H_2O)_6]^{+2}$ (A) and $[Ni(AO)_2 - H]^+$ (B).

determination of the complex composition (see Job's method, page 32).

For those ions which do not absorb in the visible region, it may be possible to use the ultraviolet region (200–390 mμ). Often the ligand absorbs, and changes may be observed in intensity and frequency due to coordination.

Hydrogen Ion Concentration Changes. Since many of the ligands which coordinate are either weak bases or acids, the hydrogen ion concentration of a solution can be used as a measure of the concentration of the uncomplexed ligand. The availability of sensitive $[H^+_{aq}]$ measuring devices, such as pH meters, makes this an attractive method for discerning complexation. Usually titration of the ligand with acid or base is employed and a comparison is made between the curves obtained with and without the metal ion present. Figure 1-4 is a graph of a titration of a mixture of the

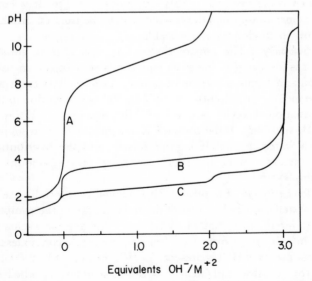

Figure 1-4. Titration Curves for $[Ni(AO)_2 - H]^+$. *A*, $[AO]_{total}$ = constant. *B*, $2[Ni^{+2}]_{total} = [AO]_{total}$ = constant. *C*, $2[Cu^{+2}]_{total} = [AO]_{total}$ = constant.

protonated ligand, AOH^+, and excess acid with NaOH (A) and similar titrations in the presence of nickel(II) (B) and copper(II) (C). When metal ions are present, the pH rises more slowly, indicating the removal of ligand into the complex. The extent of lowering is directly related to the formation constant of the complex. Thus, from the above curves, qualitatively, the formation constant for Cu^{II} is greater than that for Ni^{II}.

In a like manner, metal electrodes other than the hydrogen electrode may be used and the uncomplexed metal ion concentration directly measured. When a ligand is added to a metal ion solution, the concentration of uncomplexed metal ion decreases and is an indication of the extent of complex formation.

Optical Activity. An optically active ligand when associated with a metal ion has a different molecular rotation than when in the free state. This fact may be used to show complex formation when the complex cannot be isolated or when other methods are not applicable.

Solubility. The apparent solubility of a slightly soluble salt is increased if one of its ions bonds to a ligand in solution and forms a soluble complex. Two familiar cases are the increase in solubility of AgCl in NaI solutions due to the formation of $AgClI^-$ and the solubilization of $Cu(OH)_2$ with NH_3 solutions. If the complex is nonionic, it is often soluble in a water-immiscible organic solvent and the distribution coefficient can be used as a measure of the amount of complexation.

Ion Exchange Absorption. This method is especially useful in systems where the sign of the ionic charge of the complex is different from that of metal ion. An anionic exchange resin will not absorb Zn^{+2} from aqueous solution unless a large excess of HCl is present. In HCl the zinc is in the form of the negative ion $[ZnCl_4]^{-2}$ which is strongly absorbed on the resin. Measurements of the zinc concentration in the resin and in the aqueous phase form a good method for the determination of formation constants of $[ZnCl_4]^{-2}$.

Formulas

By convention, based upon Werner's usage, the formulas of complex ions are written with the ligands following the metal ion, all enclosed in brackets. In cases where one or more of the ligands are multiatom molecules (or ions) or are abbreviations, they are usually enclosed in parentheses—for example, $[Pt(en)_2(NO_2)Cl]^{+2}$. In ionic compounds, the formula is begun with the positive ion: $[Ni(en)_3]_3^{+2}[CoCl_6]_2^{-3}$. Because many ligands have long and cumbersome formulas, abbreviations are often used. Table 1-3 contains a list of abbreviations which will be referred to later.

The number of ligands with which a metal ion may associate depends on the metal ion, its oxidation state, and the ligand and is also affected to some extent by the environment such as temperature or solvent. In general, however, a

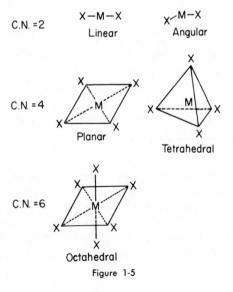

Figure 1-5

TABLE 1-3. Common Ligands

Abbreviation	Name	Formula
en	Ethylenediamine	$H_2NCH_2CH_2NH_2$
pn	Propylenediamine	$H_2NCH(CH_3)CH_2NH_2$
i-bn	Isobutylenediamine	$H_2NC(CH_3)_2CH_2NH_2$
bn	Butylenediamine	$H_2NCH(CH_3)CH(CH_3)NH_2$
tetrameen	Tetramethylethylene-diamine	$H_2NC(CH_3)_2C(CH_3)_2NH_2$
py	Pyridine	
dipy	α,α'-Dipyridyl	
o-phen	o-Phenanthroline	
EDTA	Ethylenediamine-tetraacetic acid	$\left(-CH_2N\begin{smallmatrix}CH_2COOH\\CH_2COOH\end{smallmatrix}\right)_2$
$C_2O_4{}^{-2}$	Oxalate ion	$\begin{smallmatrix}COO^-\\\|\\COO^-\end{smallmatrix}$
oxinate	Oxinate ion	
acacH	Acetylacetone	$CH_3COCH_2COCH_3$
dmgH	Dimethylglyoxime	$\begin{smallmatrix}CH_3C=NOH\\\|\\CH_3C=NOH\end{smallmatrix}$
glyH	Glycine	H_2NCH_2COOH
AO	3-Amino-3-methyl-2-butanone oxime	$NH_2C(CH_3)_2C(CH_3)=NOH$

metal in a particular oxidation state will have a constant coordination number and a particular geometry. The most common coordination numbers are 2, 4, and 6, but compounds with 3, 5, 7, and 8 are known. When the C.N. is 2, 4, 6, or 8, all of the positions are identical. Table 1-4 contains a list of some metal ions and their common coordination

TABLE 1-4. Common Coordination Numbers of Some Metal Ions

Univalent ions		Divalent ions		Trivalent ions		Tetravalent ions	
Li^+	4	Ca^{+2}	6	B^{+3}	4	Pt^{+4}	6
Na^+	4	V^{+2}	6	Al^{+3}	4, 6	Pd^{+4}	6
Ag^+	2	Fe^{+2}	6	Sc^{+3}	6		
Au^+	2, 4	Co^{+2}	4, 6	Cr^{+3}	6		
Tl^+	2	Ni^{+2}	4, 6	Fe^{+3}	6		
Cu^+	2, 4	Cu^{+2}	4, 6	Co^{+3}	6		
		Zn^{+2}	4	Os^{+3}	6		
		Pd^{+2}	4	Ir^{+3}	6		
		Pt^{+2}	4	Au^{+3}	4		
		Ag^{+2}	4				

numbers. The ligands are bound in a fixed geometry, generally one of the types found in Figure 1-5. For the less common coordination numbers (3, 5, 7, 8), other structures are taken.

If the ligand has only one potential donor atom, it is called a monodentate (one-tooth); those having more than one are multidentate ligands. If there are two positions of attachment, the ligand is a bidentate; if three, a tridentate; etc. In general five- or six-membered rings are favored and a ligand attaches through all of its donor atoms. Partially bonded ligands are never found unless there are strong steric repulsions. Coordinated multidentate ligands are spoken of

TABLE 1-5 Common Mono- and Multidentate Ligands

Ligand	Number of positions
$\overset{*}{N}H_3$	1
$\overset{*}{N}H_2CH_2CH_2\overset{*}{N}H_2$	2
$\overset{*}{N}H_2CH_2CH_2\overset{*}{N}HCH_2CH_2\overset{*}{N}H_2$	3
$\overset{*}{N}(CH_2CH_2\overset{*}{N}H_2)_3$	4
$\left(-CH_2\overset{*}{S}CH_2CH_2\overset{*}{N}=CH-\bigcirc_{-O*}\right)_2$	6

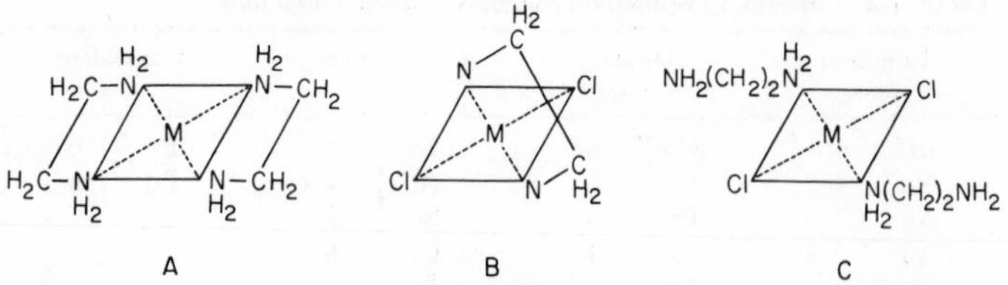

Figure 1-6

as being "chelated," and the complex is often called a chelate. These terms stem from the Greek *chele*, "claw."

Chelating ligands are only able to span *cis* positions, that is, adjacent coordination sites. For example, in the planar configuration, illustrated in Figure 1-6, only *A* forms an isolable compound. Forms *B* and *C*, if initially formed, would quickly rearrange to other species. The same is true in the octahedral configuration. Proof that bidentate ligands are chelated comes from the fact that metal ions of a known coordination number are saturated by a smaller number of chelate ligands. Cobalt(III) has a C.N. of 6 with most monodentate ligands; for example, with NH_3 it forms $[Co(NH_3)_6]^{+3}$. With en the product has the formula $[Co(en)_3]^{+3}$ and shows no tendency to associate further with NH_3, py, etc. Moreover, this chelate would be expected to associate further with H^+_{aq} if one end of the en were not attached, and this is contrary to the experimental facts. Powerful physical tools such as infrared spectroscopy show that both ends of the ligand are attached to the metal ion.

All metal ions show some tendency for coordination. Even

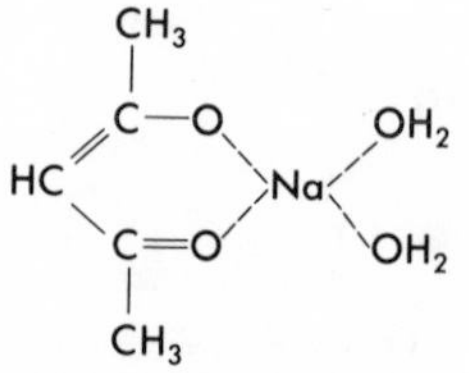

Figure 1-7

Li*	Be*											B*	Si*			F
Na*	Mg*											Al*	Si*			Cl*
K*	Ca*	Sc*	Ti*	V*	Cr*°	Mn*°	Fe°*	Co°	Ni°	Cu°	Zn°	Ga*	Ge*			Br*
Rb*	Sr*	Y*	Zr*	Nb*	Mo*	Tc*°	Ru°	Rh°	Pd°	Ag°	Cd°	In*	Sn*	Sb*	Te	I*
		La*	Hf*	Ta*	W*	Re*	Os°	Ir°	Pt°	Au°	Hg°*	Tl*	Pb*	Bi*	Po	

Figure 1-8. * = oxygen, fluorine; ° = nitrogen, phosphorus, sulfur.

alkali and alkaline earth metal ions possess this quality. It has been demonstrated that sodium ion forms the type of complex shown in Figure 1-7. Elements may be classified in a qualitative way according to the types of coordinating atoms they prefer (Fig. 1-8).

The list of common donor atoms is shorter and is limited to the more electronegative atoms in groups IV, V, VI, and VII: C, N, O, F, Cl, Br, I, P, S, As. Neutral *atoms* are seldom if ever ligands. Usually the donor atom is present as a negative ion or is in a covalent molecule. The ability of a ligand to coordinate is determined to a large extent by the atoms or groups present in it, their electronegativity, and steric factors. Often a close relationship exists between the basic properties of the ligand with respect to H^+_{aq} and the tendency to coordinate with a metal ion.

Naming

The number and variety of coordination compounds make it impossible to name, by one set of rules, all of the compounds which have been prepared. General rules have been formulated, however, and are useful in the majority of cases. A complex ion may be either a neutral molecule (e.g., $[Pt(NH_3)_2Cl_2]^0$), a positive ion (e.g., $[Zn(NH_3)_4]^{+2}$), or a negative ion (e.g., $[ReCl_6]^{-2}$).

Rule 1. If a complex contains ions, the full name of the positive ion is given first, followed by the full name of the negative ion. Note that the ion names are separated by a space and the number of each type of ion is not indicated.

$K_2[PtCl_6]$	Potassium hexachloroplatinum(IV)
$[Cr(H_2O)_6](ClO_4)_3$	Hexaquochromium(III) perchlorate

Rule 2. For each ion, the order of presentation is ligands, metal, and oxidation state in Roman numerals.*

$[Co(NH_3)_6]Cl_3$ Hexamminecobalt(III) chloride
$K_2[ZnCl_4]$ Potassium tetrachlorozinc(II)

Rule 3. Many complexes contain more than one type of ligand. The order is negative before neutral before positive, and multiatom ligands before simple. Usually NH_3 (ammine) is the last to be named.

$[Co(NH_3)_4(NO_2)Cl]ClO_4$ Nitrochlorotetramminecobalt(III) perchlorate
$[Pt(en)(NH_3)_2(SCN)_2]Cl_2$ Dithiocyanato(ethylenediamine)-diammineplatinum(IV) chloride

Halo substituents are named according to increasing electronegativity, I^- before Br^- before Cl^- before F^-, and all coordinated negative ions end in -o- (chloro, nitro, thiocyanato, sulfato).

Rule 4. When the number of ligands of one type is greater than one, the prefixes *di-*, *tri-*, *tetra-*, *penta-*, *hexa-*, etc., are used. If the group has a complicated structure, the prefixes *bis-*, *tris-*, *tetrakis-*, etc., are used, and the group is enclosed in parentheses.

$[Co(NH_3)_5H_2O]I_3$ Aquopentamminecobalt(III) iodide
$[Ir(en)_2(NH_3)_2]Cl_3$ Bis(ethylenediamine)diammine-iridium(III) chloride

Rule 5. Bridges are denoted by μ. The compound to the right contains two hydroxyl bridges, each coordinated to two metal ions, and is called bis(ethylenediamine) - μ - dihydroxodicopper(II) chloride.

Rule 6. In compounds containing metal-to-metal bonds, the prefix *bi-* is used.

---

*Many authors prefer to use the ending *-ate* for a negatively charged complex ion; for example, $K_2[CoCl_4]$ may be named potassium tetrachlorocobaltate(II).

$$\left[(CH_3NH_2)_4 \underset{\underset{Cl}{|}}{Pt} - \underset{\underset{Cl}{|}}{Pt}(NH_2CH_3)_4 \right]^{+2} \quad 2\,Cl^-$$

sym-Dichlorooctakis(methylamine)biplatinum(II) chloride

Rule 7. Geometrical isomers are named using the prefixes *cis-* or *trans-* or, where the structure is complex, by a numbering system.

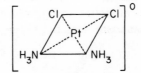

Potassium *cis*-dinitrodichloro-
platinum(II)

trans-Dinitrobis(ethylenediamine)cobalt(III) chloride

1,2-Dichlorodiammineplatinum(II)

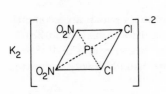

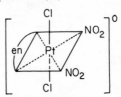

2,3-Dinitro-1,6-dichloro(ethylenediamine)platinum(IV)

Rule 8. Some ligands may attach using more than one atom. Then the attached atom is specified.

M—SCN   Thiocyanato-S-
M—NCS   Thiocyanato-N-

Rule 9. When a complex or ligand is optically active, *d* and *l* refer to the direction of rotation (right and left, respectively) and D or L refer to the genetic configurations. If the complex is optically active, the prefix precedes the name; while if the ligand is active, the prefix precedes *its* name: d-[Co(en)$_2$Cl$_2$]Cl and [Co(l-pn)$_3$]Cl$_3$.

Stereoisomerism

In coordination compounds both geometric and optical isomerism occurs. We will discuss the general aspects of the topic which apply to all coordination numbers and configurations.

Geometrical Isomers. Two substances which are geometrical isomers have identical empirical formulas but differ in chemical and physical properties because of the different arrangement of atoms. They are usually easily separated by chemical or physical means.

Cis-trans isomers may be illustrated with planar and octahedral complexes. In a *cis-* attachment two identical groups are adjacent to each other; in a *trans-* attachment the two identical groups are opposite each other (Fig. 1-9). This type of isomerism does not occur with tetrahedral coordination.

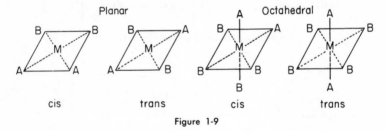

Figure 1-9

Cis-trans isomers can also occur with unsymmetrical bidentate ligands in the planar and octahedral configuration (Fig. 1-10).

Optical Isomerism. A complex which does not have a plane of symmetry is potentially optically active. When prepared in a usual laboratory manner from optically inactive reagents, it will consist of equal amounts of the d and l isomers. Under favorable circumstances these can be separated, and

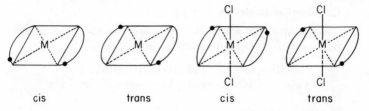

Figure 1-10

by definition the *d* form rotates a plane of light to the right, while the *l* form rotates to the left. Except for this one property *d* and *l* forms are identical in physical and chemical properties, but the *dl* mixture often has slightly different properties. Tetrahedral systems of the type M(abcd) are capable of optical isomerism. In the planar state few examples are known. A molecule which was used to demonstrate the planar state is of the type shown in Figure 1-11. It is well to note that the analogous tetrahedral configuration has a plane of symmetry and cannot be optically active. In the octahedral configuration, ions of the type cis-$[M(en)_2X_2]^0$ and $[M(en)_3]^{+2}$ consist of *d* and *l* isomers, but $trans$-$[M(en)_2X_2]^0$ does not.

Figure 1-11

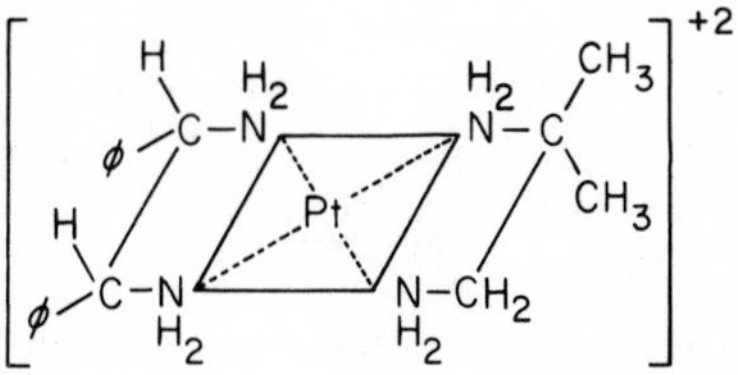

Ionization Isomerism

Compounds which have the same composition but differ in the number or type of ions produced fall into this category. For example

$$[Co(en)_2(NO_2)Cl]Cl \quad and \quad [Co(en)_2Cl_2]NO_2$$

Coordination Isomerism

In compounds where two ions are complex, the ligands may be distributed differently, giving isomers.

$[Cu(NH_3)_4][PtCl_4]$ and $[Pt(NH_3)_4][CuCl_4]$

$[Cr(en)_3][Co(ox)_3]$ and $[Cr(en)_2(ox)][Co(ox)_2(en)]$

Linkage Isomerism

In some instances a ligand may attach through either of two atoms. The best known is with nitrite ion. It may attach through an oxygen or nitrogen.

$[Co(NH_3)_5—ONO]Cl_2$ *or* $[Co(NH_3)_5—NO_2]Cl_2$

Nitrito *or* nitro-O   Nitrato *or* nitro-N

Also thiocyanates may attach through either nitrogen or sulfur.

Ligand Isomerism

Many ligands are themselves capable of existing as isomeric states. In the butylenediamine system the geometrical forms in Figure 1-12 (*A–E*) are known as well as *N*-methyl types such as Figure 1-12*F*. When these ligands are associated into complexes, the complexes are isomers of each other.

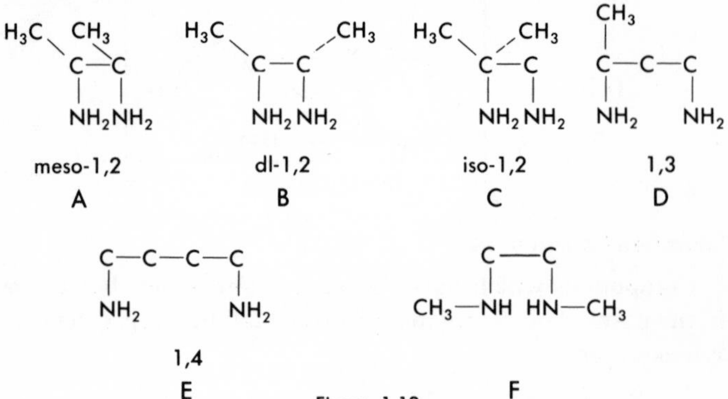

Figure 1-12

THERMODYNAMIC
STABILITY

IN ORDER TO understand the relationships in coordinate bonding and to be able to predict unknown reactions, it is necessary to have quantitative measurements on the degree of metal-ligand association. For this purpose, systems which are labile (that is, come to equilibrium quickly) are especially useful. This is not to imply that quantitative information about nonlabile systems is not important, but rather that the experimental measurements are somewhat more difficult when equilibrium is reached slowly.

The majority of quantitative equilibrium measurements have been carried out in aqueous solution because of enhanced solubilities and because more is known about how ions behave in this solvent. In water, the reactants (metal ion and ligand) as well as the product complex are hydrated to some unknown extent. Neglecting the somewhat smaller hydration energy of the ligand, we have in complex formation a displacement of water molecules by ligands:

$$[M(H_2O)_n]^{+y} + L \rightleftharpoons [M(H_2O)_{n-1}L]^{+y} + H_2O \quad (2\text{-}1)$$

With monodentate ligands one water molecule is usually replaced for each ligand attached: with a bidentate ligand, two. It is important that we recognize that formation reactions in aqueous solution are always of the replacement type. For most metal ions, the number of water molecules attached directly to the metal is not accurately known but is often presumed to be four for small ions and six for larger ions. In addition to the "inner sphere" of solvent molecules, an additional association takes place in the "second sphere." This association is relatively weak and occurs through hydrogen bonding to the water molecules in the "inner sphere." In our discussion, we will neglect the coordinated water of the metal ion in order to simplify the equations.

Two concepts which apply universally to coordination equilibria are *stepwise formation* and *chelate stability*. In the first of these, it is found that a complex ion containing several ligands forms, by successively adding ligands, and usually the first association is stronger than the second, the second stronger than the third, etc. Experiments have shown that with chelating ligands, the half-bonded structures are not nearly as stable as chelated structures. Thus equilibria of type 2-2 do not have to be considered because the product of reaction 2-3 is much more stable.

$$M^{+2} + NH_2CH_2CH_2NH_2 \rightarrow [M{-}NH_2CH_2CH_2NH_2]^{+2} \quad (2\text{-}2)$$

$$M^{+2} + NH_2CH_2CH_2NH_2 \rightarrow \begin{bmatrix} M \begin{smallmatrix} \diagup NH_2 \diagdown CH_2 \\ \quad | \\ \diagdown NH_2 \diagup CH_2 \end{smallmatrix} \end{bmatrix}^{+2} \quad (2\text{-}3)$$

The equilibria involved in the formation of complexes of a metal ion, M^{+y}, and a neutral ligand, L, are given by:

$$M^{+y} + L \rightleftharpoons ML^{+y}$$
$$ML^{+y} + L \rightleftharpoons ML_2{}^{+y}$$
$$\vdots$$
$$ML_{n-1}{}^{+y} + L \rightleftharpoons ML_n{}^{+y}$$

The overall formation is

$$M^{+y} + nL \rightarrow ML_n{}^{+y} \quad (2\text{-}4)$$

Each reaction is governed by an equilibrium constant (2-5)

$$K_1 = [ML^{+y}]/[M^{+y}][L]$$

$$K_2 = [ML_2^{+y}]/[ML^{+y}][L]$$

$$\vdots$$

$$K_n = [ML_n^{+y}]/[ML_{n-1}^{+y}][L] \qquad (2\text{-}5)$$

which, if written for the formation reaction, is commonly called the *formation constant*. The overall formation constant is given by β_n (2-5a)   For most complexes $K_1 > K_2 >$

$$\beta_n = [ML_n^{+y}]/[M^{+y}][L]^n \qquad (2\text{-}5a)$$

$K_3 > \cdots > K_n$ and the overall formation constant is

$$\beta_n = K_1 K_2 K_3 \cdots K_n \qquad (2\text{-}5b)$$

A more useful manner of stating equilibrium constants is in terms of the standard free energy change, $\Delta G°$. This is the difference in free energy between the products and the reactants in a standard state and is related to the equilibrium constant by the expression:

$$\Delta G° = -RT \ln K \qquad (2\text{-}6)$$

where $\Delta G°$ is in cal/mole; R is the gas law constant (1.987 cal/deg mole); T is the absolute temperature; and K is the equilibrium constant. $\Delta G°$ is a measure of the tendency of a reaction to go in the direction written and is composed of two terms: the heat change, $\Delta H°$, and the entropy change, $\Delta S°$. The relationship between these quantities is given by:

$$\Delta G° = \Delta H° - T \Delta S° \qquad (2\text{-}7)$$

When $\Delta G°$ is negative, the reaction tends to go in the direction written; when positive, in the opposite direction. $\Delta H°$, often called the enthalpy change, has units of cal/mole, while the entropy change has units of cal/°A. $\Delta H°$ is the amount of heat either consumed or liberated per mole of product and is related to the strength of the ligand-to-metal bonds compared to that of the metal-to-solvent bonds. When it is negative, heat is liberated and the products are warmer than the reactants. The entropy change relates to the amount of order in the products compared to that in the reactants. When $\Delta S°$ is positive, it contributes to a more negative free energy change, and the products are less ordered than the reactants.

The heat of reaction may be measured directly or may be determined by the variation of the equilibrium constant with temperature. Equation 2-8 allows a calculation of $\Delta H°$ from the values of K at two temperatures. Values of $\Delta G°$ and $\Delta H°$ may thus be obtained experimentally, and from these values we can calculate $\Delta S°$.

$$\ln (K_2/K_1) = (\Delta H°/R)(T_2 - T_1)/T_2 T_1 \qquad (2\text{-}8)$$

Although the concept of formation constants is in principle simple, there are many experimental difficulties involved in obtaining precise, meaningful values. There seem to be two areas which cause most of the difficulty: activity coefficients (γ) and the determination of the actual species present.

In the strictest sense the formation constant is derived from activities of ions rather than concentrations, and the formation constant should be written as in 2-9. Since the activ-

$$M^{+y} + L \rightleftharpoons ML^{+y} \qquad K_1 = A_{ML^{+y}}/A_{M^{+y}} A_L \quad (2\text{-}9)$$

ity (A) is defined as equal to the product of the activity coefficient and the concentration, the equilibrium constant becomes:

$$K_1 = \gamma_{ML^{+y}}[ML^{+y}]/\gamma_{M^{+y}}[M^{+y}]\gamma_L[L] \qquad (2\text{-}10)$$

In most experimental situations the concentrations of the species can be determined, but the activity coefficients cannot. Several ways of overcoming this difficulty are used: (*1*) Determine the equilibrium constant at various total concentrations, and extrapolate K to zero total concentration.

This is based on the fact that the activity coefficients approach unity as the concentration approaches zero, and thus the concentration equilibrium constant equals the activity equilibrium constant. (2) Calculate the activity coefficients using the extended Debye-Hückel equation. (3) Carry out the equilibrium constant determination in a large excess (0.1–1.0M) of inert salt such as $NaClO_4$. Because the salt concentration does not vary at various positions in the equilibria, the activity coefficients are thought to remain essentially constant. Thus one obtains concentration constants which are constant, and comparisons between various metals or ligands can be made. Unfortunately, however, a comparison with another ionic medium is not possible because the activity coefficients will not be the same.

The second problem—the determination of the formulas of the species actually present—often is less difficult to solve. One cannot determine an equilibrium constant for a reaction unless the stoichiometry of the reaction is known. Sometimes in simple cases the constancy of an experimental formation constant may be used as evidence that the equilibrium quotient is the proper one. In most cases, however, outside evidence from other experimental methods must be used to establish which of the many possible equilibria are important.

Measurement of Formation Constants

The selection of the best method of determining the formation constant of a complex is usually made on the basis of the experimenter's experience. For the greatest reliability, the results of more than one method should be compared. A discussion of all the methods which have been used and an explanation of the complications arising from multiple equilibria would fill a lengthy book, and we will restrict ourselves to the most useful methods and to single equilibria in most cases. Among the numerous other methods, polarography, immiscible solvent distribution coefficients, conductance, refractive index, temperature and volume changes, nuclear magnetic resonance, magnetic moment changes, and optical activity are useful in specialized situations, but the general ideas to be developed here apply.

Solubility Method. If the metal ion forms a relatively insoluble salt whose solubility product is known and a complex which is rather more soluble, the formation constant of the complex may be determined by measuring the increased solubility of the salt caused by the presence of the ligand. Consider the reaction of silver acetate with acetate ion. If a sodium acetate solution of known high concentration is equilibrated at constant temperature with an excess of silver acetate, the equilibria given in 2-11 are satisfied. (In a basic medium the hydrolysis of acetate ion may be neglected.)

$$AgOAc \rightleftharpoons Ag^+ + OAc^-$$

$$K_{sp} = [Ag^+][OAc^-]$$

$$Ag^+ + 2\,OAc^- \rightleftharpoons Ag(OAc)_2^-$$

$$\beta_2 = [Ag(OAc)_2^-]/[Ag^+][OAc^-]^2 \qquad (2\text{-}11)$$

After equilibration, the excess solid silver acetate is removed by filtration and the solution analyzed for total silver. Then the following relationship holds

$$C_{Ag^+} = [Ag^+] + [Ag(OAc)_2^-] \qquad (2\text{-}12)$$

where C_{Ag^+} is the solution silver concentration. From the solubility product expression we get $[Ag^+] = K_{sp}/[OAc^-]$, and this becomes

$$[Ag^+] = K_{sp}/C_{NaOAc} \qquad (2\text{-}13)$$

because of the large excess of sodium acetate. Substituting equations 2-12 and 2-13 in the formation constant expression gives

$$\beta_2 = (C_{Ag^+} - K_{sp}/C_{NaOAc})/[(K_{sp}/C_{NaOAc}) \cdot (C_{NaOAc})^2] \qquad (2\text{-}14)$$

Each of these quantities is known, and the overall formation constant β_2 may be calculated. Of course it is necessary to vary the sodium acetate concentration to see if β_2 is really a constant, and further refinements would take into account the hydrolysis of acetate ion and the loss of free OAc^- through complexation.

Spectral Method. Most complexes absorb light differently than the metal ions from which they are formed. The relationship between the absorbance (A) is at a particular wavelength of light and concentration is Beers' law:

$$A = \log(I_0/I) = \epsilon l c \qquad (2\text{-}15)$$

where ϵ is the molar extinction coefficient; l is the length of the absorption cell; and c is the concentration in moles/liter. If one measures the absorbance with a spectrophotometer and knows the extinction coefficient at that wavelength, and the cell length, the concentration can be calculated. Representative spectra of a metal and its complex might be as

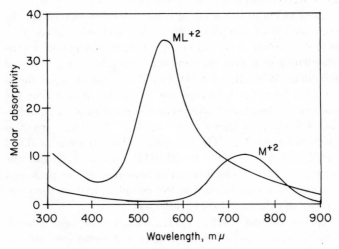

Figure 2-1. Spectral Changes on Coordination.

shown in Fig. 2-1. Note that absorption by the complex takes place over the entire region of metal ion absorption while at 550 mμ only the complex absorbs. In order to obtain the formation constant for the reaction $M^{+2} + L \overset{K_F}{\rightleftharpoons} ML^{+2}$, solutions containing known amounts of total M^{+2} and total L are equilibrated. The absorption of these solutions at 550 mμ is measured and the formation constant evaluated. Equations 2-16 apply where C_M and C_L are total concentrations of all forms of the metal ion and ligand. Since A,

$$C_M = [M^{+2}] + [ML^{+2}]$$
$$C_L = [L] + [ML^{+2}] \qquad (2\text{-}16)$$
$$A = \epsilon_{(ML^{+2})} l [ML^{+2}]$$

$\epsilon_{(ML^{+2})}$, and l are known, $[ML^{+2}]$ can be found. Using the known values for C_M and C_L, we obtain the $[M^{+2}]$ and $[L]$, and combining these in the formation constant expression gives K_F. The constancy of K_F is checked by repeating the measurements at different C_M and C_L values.

A variation of this method is often used to determine the composition of complex ions. This method, called *Job's method*, involves a measurement of light absorption at the wavelength of maximum complex absorption for a series of solutions. When the sum of the total concentrations of metal ion plus ligand is held constant, it can be shown that the maximum absorbance will occur when the ratio of ligand to metal is equal to that in the complex. A typical graph is given in Figure 2-2. The maximum absorbance is at 0.333 metal to 0.666 L; thus the [L]/[M] ratio is 2:1, and the formula is ML_2. The amount of rounding at the peak is a measure of the instability of the complex, and in some instances may be used to determine K_F.

Bjerrum Method. When the ligand is a weak base or acid, competition between hydrogen ions and metal ions for the ligand can be used to an advantage. This comes about be-

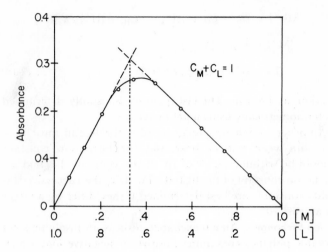

Figure 2-2. Job's Method of Continuous Variation.

cause the concentration of hydrogen ions can be accurately measured while often the concentration of the metal ions and ligands cannot. If we consider the equilibria involved when acid and metal ion are placed in a solution containing a basic ligand, using C_H, C_M, and C_L to be the total amounts in moles/liter of these added, then equations 2-17 follow.

$$L \; + \; H^+ \; \rightleftharpoons \; HL^+ \quad K_a \; = \; [HL^+]/[L][H^+]$$

$$L \; + \; M^+ \; \rightleftharpoons \; ML^+ \quad K_1 \; = \; [ML^+]/[M^+][L]$$

$$C_H \; = \; [H^+] \; + \; [HL^+]$$

$$C_L \; = \; [L] \; + \; [ML^+] \; + \; [HL^+]$$

$$C_M \; = \; [M^+] \; + \; [ML^+] \tag{2-17}$$

Solving the last three equations of 2-17 using the acid association constant of the ligand, K_a, gives 2-18. Thus all of the concentrations necessary for the formation constant can be determined if C_H, C_L, C_M, K_a, and the hydrogen ion concen-

$$[ML^+] = C_L - C_H + [H^+] - (C_H - [H^+])/K_a[H^+]$$

$$[M^+] = C_M - [ML^+]$$

$$[L] = (C_H - [H^+])/K_a[H^+] \tag{2-18}$$

tration are known. The last quantity is usually determined potentiometrically using a pH meter.

In order to achieve precise results, the ligand must be a medium weak acid or base and the formation constant should be within a factor of 10^5 of the value of the acid association constant of the ligand. Further, the successive stability constants are best determined if they differ by a factor of at least 10^2.

Ion Exchange. An ion exchange resin is an insoluble solid organic polymer containing positive or negative ions which are exchangeable. If a cationic resin is in contact with a solution of sodium and calcium ions, an equilibrium constant (2-19) may be written. If the amount of dipositive

$$K_r = [Na^+]^2_{soln}[Ca^{+2}]_{resin}/[Na^+]^2_{resin}[Ca^{+2}]_{soln} \tag{2-19}$$

ion is small compared to $[Na^+]$, the Na^+ concentration in both phases remains nearly constant and equation 2-20 results.

$$K_r' = [Ca^{+2}]_{resin}/[Ca^{+2}]_{soln} \tag{2-20}$$

Upon addition of a ligand such as citrate ion to the above solution, the concentration of free Ca^{+2} decreases because [Ca citrate]$^-$ is formed and thus the amount of Ca^{+2} in the resin decreases. The formation constant is given by equation 2-21; and the distribution quotient, D, is defined by 2-22.

$$K_F = [Ca\,citrate^-]/[Ca^{+2}][citrate^{-3}] \tag{2-21}$$

$$D = [Ca^{+2}]_{resin}/([Ca^{+2}]_{soln} + [Ca\,citrate^-]_{soln}) \tag{2-22}$$

From these we obtain the useful equation 2-23.

$$1/D = K_F[citrate^{-3}]/K_r' + 1/K_r' \tag{2-23}$$

Since D can be measured at various citrate ion concentrations and since this is an equation of the form $y = mx + b$, a graph of $1/D$ versus [citrate^{-3}] produces a straight line with a slope of K_F/K_r' and an intercept of $1/K_r'$. From the slope and intercept K_F may be determined. This is an especially fast and easy method for the determination of formation constants. The total concentration of metal in the resin phase as well as that in the liquid phase can most conveniently be determined if the metal is radioactive. Therefore, this method is usually applied to systems where a suitable radioactive metal ion isotope is available.

Isotopic Method. If a complex ion is slow to reach equilibrium, it is often possible to apply the method of isotopic dilution to determine the equilibrium concentration of one or more of the species. Most often radioactive isotopes are used, but stable isotopes such as O^{18}, N^{15}, and deuterium may be valuable in certain cases. In principle, the method consists of allowing an equilibrium to be reached between the inactive metal and ligand; adding a known amount of metal ion, ligand, or complex in a radioactive form; and quickly separating the species which was added. The activity of the separated species is a measure of the amount of that species initially present at equilibrium. Consider the reaction between Cr^{+3} and Cl^- which has the slow kinetics necessary for this type of study. If a solution of $[Cr(H_2O)_6](ClO_4)_3$ and HCl is allowed to come to equilibrium according to equation 2-24, and the amount of Cl^- is relatively low so that

$$Cr^{+3} + Cl^- \rightleftharpoons CrCl^{+2} \qquad (2\text{-}24)$$

$[CrCl_2]^+$ is not formed in appreciable amounts, then

$$[Cr^{+3}] = C_{Cr^{+3}} - [CrCl^{+2}]$$
$$[CrCl^{+2}] = C_{Cl^-} - [Cl^-] \qquad (2\text{-}25)$$

where $C_{Cr^{+3}}$ and C_{Cl^-} refer to the concentrations of these substances assuming no complex formation. If [Cl$^-$] at equilibrium can be found, then the formation constant can be evaluated.

If a known amount of Cl^{36} is added giving an additional $[Cl^-]$ of $C^*_{Cl^-}$ and the Cl^- is precipitated with Ag^+ without removing from or exchanging with $[CrCl]^{+2}$, then equation 2-26 holds. A_0 is the radioactivity of the undiluted $AgCl^{36}$,

$$[Cl^-] = (C^*_{Cl^-})[(A_0/A_M) + 1] \qquad (2\text{-}26)$$

and A_M, that of the AgCl obtained from the reaction mixture, in disintegrations per minute per gram of AgCl. The concentration of chloride ion not complexed thus may be used directly to give the formation constant.

Various ramifications of this method have been used, but they are applicable only to systems in which the reactions are slow, and where the addition of the radioactive substance does not change the position of the equilibrium during the period of isolation. Also, the reagent used for separation must not induce exchange. Statistical variations as well as other factors usually limit the precision of radioactive activity determination, but the method may be designed to give 1% precision even with extremely small concentrations of the measured ion. In spite of the limitations of this method, isotopic dilution provides a useful means of formation constant determination in certain systems.

Electromotive Force Method. A metal in contact with a solution of its ions gives a potential, E, which is governed by equation 2-27. If two different cells of this type are

$$E = E^\circ - (RT/nF) \ln ([M^{+2}]/[M]_{solid}) \qquad (2\text{-}27)$$

connected, the voltage is the difference of the two cell potentials and can be measured with high precision (Fig. 2-3). If the cells are identical—i.e., both the same metal and the same metal ion concentration—then the measured voltage will be zero. Should a ligand be added to cell 1, the complex equilibria (2-28) will cause a change in the free metal ion

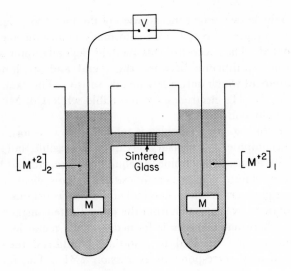

Figure 2-3. Stability Constant Determination by Potential Measurement.

$$M^{+2} + L \rightleftharpoons ML^{+2} \qquad (2\text{-}28)$$

concentration and a net voltage will be observed. The observed voltage is given by 2-29 or 2-30

$$E_{\text{obs}} = E_1 - E_2$$
$$= -(RT/nF)[\ln([M^{+2}]_1/[M]_{\text{solid}}) - \ln([M^{+2}]_2/[M]_{\text{solid}})] \quad (2\text{-}29)$$

$$E_{\text{obs}} = -(RT/nF)\ln([M^{+2}]_1/[M^{+2}]_2) \qquad (2\text{-}30)$$

where T is the absolute temperature; R is the gas law constant (8.3 joules/deg mole); F is the Faraday (96,500 coulombs); and n is the number of electrons transferred, in this case ($M^0 \rightarrow M^{+2}$) equal to 2. Thus the observed voltage is directly related to the free metal ion concentrations in the cells. If $[M^{+2}]_2$ is known, $[M^{+2}]_1$ may be calculated. In practice, successive portions of ligand are added to the metal ion solution in one cell and the corresponding voltages measured.

From the known total concentration of the metal ion, ligand, and uncomplexed metal ion, the formation constant may be evaluated. The success of this method depends upon a reversible equilibrium between the metal and its ions, a requirement which only a few metals satisfy. For example, Cu, Ag, Ni, Hg electrodes are reversible while Co, Mn, Fe are usually not.

Rate Method. If a complex is relatively slow to form and also decomposes at a measurable rate, it is possible, in favorable situations, to determine the equilibrium constant. Often the rates of formation or decomposition are complicated and consist of several paths. The individual rate constants must be obtained by separation from the overall rate constant. In cases where one complex is formed and the metal ion and ligand are not involved in acid-base equilibria, the rate forward may correspond to expression 2-31. The reverse

$$\text{rate}_F \quad = \quad k_F[M^+][L] \qquad (2\text{-}31)$$

reaction may have simple first order kinetics and equation 2-32 applies. If k_F and k_B can be determined, they may

$$\text{rate}_B \quad = \quad k_B[ML^+] \qquad (2\text{-}32)$$

be used to evaluate K_F from expression 2-33. This follows

$$k_F/k_B \quad = \quad K_F \quad = \quad [ML^+]/[M^+][L] \qquad (2\text{-}33)$$

from the rate expressions and the fact that, at equilibrium, $\text{rate}_F = \text{rate}_B$. The main problem with this method comes in the conversion of the experimentally determined rates into rate constants.

Stability Relationships at Equilibrium

The magnitude of stability constants varies over wide extremes, usually between 10^{-5} and 10^{+30}. In order to facilitate the comparison of these values they are usually given in terms of log K_F.

For a comparison of the strength of bonding it would be useful to have formation constants for reaction 2-34. These

$$M^{+2}_{gas} + L_{gas} \rightleftharpoons [ML]^{+2}_{gas} \qquad (2\text{-}34)$$

cannot be determined directly, but in certain cases they may be calculated from aqueous stability constants. These calculations are beyond the scope of this book, however, and we will have to be content with replacement reactions in which a ligand replaces one or more water molecules.

At this point it is well to emphasize that formation constants provide a means of comparing stabilities *at equilibrium* and may be very misleading in attempts to predict reactions. For example, on the basis of the equilibrium constant for reaction 2-35, one might expect the addition of excess

$$[(Co(en)_3]^{+3} + 6H^+ \rightleftharpoons [Co(H_2O)_x]^{+3} + 3[(en)H_2]^{+2} \quad K \approx 10^{30} \ (2\text{-}35)$$

acid to $[Co(en)_3]^{+3}$ to give $[Co(H_2O)_x]^{+3}$ nearly quantitatively. Experiment shows, however, that after one month at room temperatures less than 1% of the reaction occurs. Thus, this reaction is controlled by the kinetics. In the presence of a catalyst, however, the reaction goes quickly to equilibrium and almost all of the cobalt is in the form of $[Co(H_2O)_x]^{+3}$.

Ligand Effects. The majority of coordination compounds contain nitrogen, oxygen, sulfur, or a halogen as the bonding atom. Some metals which prefer oxygen over nitrogen are Mg^{+2}, Ca^{+2}, Si^{+4}, Sn^{+2}, U^{+5}, U^{+6}, Fe^{+3}, and Be^{+2}. Some which prefer nitrogen donors to those of oxygen are Cu^+, Cu^{+2}, Ag^+, Au^+, Cd^{+2}, Hg^{+2}, V^{+2}, Co^{+3}, and Ni^{+2}. There is also a group which seems to coordinate equally well with either oxygen or nitrogen: Cr^{+3}, Fe^{+2}, Pt^{+4}, Zn^{+2}, and Re^{+5}. Except for Cu^+, Ag^+, Au^+, and Hg^{+2}, oxygen donors are clearly superior to those of sulfur. These facts may be rationalized on the basis of the metal ion charge in the complex. If coordination involves the donation of a pair of electrons from the ligand to the metal ion, a considerable negative charge results on the metal atom. This is contrary to the behavior of metal ions and would result in an unstable condition. The system may achieve stability by having only partial donation of electron pairs and a metal ion charge of nearly zero. The "ionic potential" (charge/radius) is a measure of the tendency of a metal ion to associate with electron pairs, while the polarizability of a ligand is related to its ability to donate electron pairs. At first glance it would appear that high ionic potential and high polarizability would give the most stable complexes. However, as these two quantities increase, a point is reached where the resultant negative charge on the metal ion opposes electron transfer, thus causing a lower stability. Thus it is often found that a maximum is reached at some position in this series: F, O, N, S, P. For many first transition metals of low oxidation state (low I.P.) the maximum is at nitrogen, while for higher oxidation states and small size, oxygen compounds have the maximum stability. With certain large ions of low charge (Cu^+, Ag^+, Au^+, Hg^+) the maximum occurs with sulfur-containing ligands.

Another method of removing the negative charge on the central metal atom is through a lower coordination number. Many metal ions of high oxidation state lower the charge on the metal ion in this manner, for example, CrO_4^{-2}, $CoCl_4^{-2}$, $NiCl_4^{-2}$.

Ions which have eight or ten d electrons often have little tendency to become positively charged and thus are able to accept electrons from ligands. Such ions as Hg^{+2}, Au^+, Ag^+, Pd^{+2}, and Pt^{+2} form more stable complexes with ligands of high polarizability and $P > S > N > O$. Also with these ions, the order of stability is $I > Br > Cl > F$, which is just the opposite of that observed for almost all other metal ions.

Many different atomic groupings are possible for ligands; they are limited only by the organic chemist's ability to prepare them. Some of the more important groups are in Table 2-1.

TABLE 2-1

$\begin{array}{c} R \\ \diagdown \\ O \\ \diagup \\ R \end{array}$	$RC\diagup^{\displaystyle O}_{\diagdown O^-}$	$\begin{array}{c} R \\ \diagdown \\ C{=}O \\ \diagup \\ R \end{array}$	$\begin{array}{c} O \\ \| \\ R{-}S{-}O^- \\ \| \\ O \end{array}$
R_3N	$R_2N{-}NR_2$	$R{=}N{-}OH$	$R_2{-}C{=}NH$
R_2S	RSH	$R_2{-}C{=}S$	

It is almost universally found that alkyl substitution for a hydrogen decreases the stability of the complex. Thus, we can expect the following orders of stability: $NH_3 > CH_3NH_2 > (CH_3)_2NH > (CH_3)_3N$ and $H_2O > CH_3OH > (CH_3)_2O$. However, for sulfur the opposite trend is observed, the order of stability being $R_2S > RSH > H_2S$.

The associations of a ligand with a metal ion and with hydrogen ion are analogous situations, and, to a first approximation at least, strongly basic substances would be expected also to have large association constants with metal ions. This is often found to be the case for closely related ligands where the bond type is the same. For many metal ions, the observed stability sequence is the same as the base strength order: $F^- > NO_3^- > Cl^- > Br^- > I^- > ClO_4^- = BF_4^-$. Moreover, a comparison of the stability constants of primary amines with Ag^+ gives the values in Table 2-2. It is interesting to note (Fig. 2-4) that primary, secondary, and tertiary amines may not be directly compared in the relationship between complex stability and basicity, but linear relationships between base strength and coordinating ability

TABLE 2-2

	$\log K_{F(av)}$ (Ag^+)	pK_a
CH_3NH_2	3.34	10.72
$C_2H_5NH_2$	3.65	10.81
$C_3H_7NH_2$	3.84	10.92
$C_4H_9NH_2$	3.74	10.72

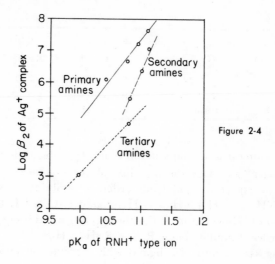

Figure 2-4

are obtained for each type of amine. The lower stability of the complexes of secondary and tertiary amines is attributed to steric hindrance between the ligands. Similar linear relationships have been observed with ethylenediamines, β-diketones, α-ketoesters, and amino acids. (Thus it may be said that, other things being equal, the more basic the amine, the more stable the complex.)

Along the same line, a ligand of high coordinating ability with one metal ion should be also preferred by *another* metal ion. Using this line of reasoning, a graph of $\log K$ for one ligand versus $\log K'$ for another ligand should be linear for *many* metal ions if the ligands form similar type bonds and

TABLE 2-3

		en	N,N'-di-Me-en	N,N'-di-Et-en
Ni^{II}	$\log K_1$	7.60	7.11	5.62
	$\log K_2$	6.48	4.73	3.3
	$\log K_3$	5.03	1.5	Very small
Cu^{II}	$\log K_1$	11.34	11.22	10.84
	$\log K_2$	9.95	8.31	7.85

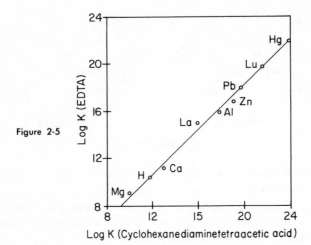

Figure 2-5

Log K (EDTA)

Log K (Cyclohexanediaminetetraacetic acid)

have identical stereochemistry. In selected cases, such as that shown in Figure 2-5, this is true.

The steric effect in decreasing the stability of a complex has already been noted with substituted amines. Table 2-3 lists the observations made on ethylenediamine complexes of Cu^{II} and Ni^{II}. The base strength of the amines remains nearly constant, but the stability constants decrease with increasing substitution of methyl groups. The steric factor is especially apparent in K_2 and K_3 because of methyl-methyl group repulsions between coordinated substituted ethylene-diamines. Similarly, it has been shown that acetylacetonates of Cu^{II} and Fe^{II} do not form when the substituent at the 3 position is an isopropyl group, but that typical chelates do form when it is a straight chain group (Fig. 2-6).

The stereochemical requirements of the ligand often affect stability. The ligand *tren*, $N(CH_2CH_2NH_2)_3$, is unable to coordinate to four planar positions but may do so to four tetrahedral positions. *Trien*, $H_2N(CH_2)_2NH(CH_2)_2-NH(CH_2)_2NH_2$, however, is more suited to a planar arrange-

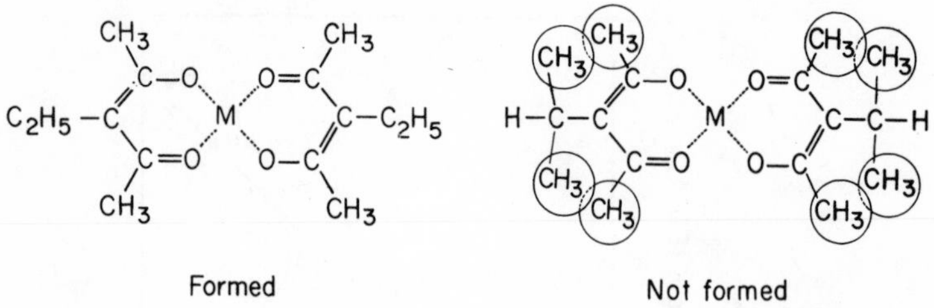

Figure 2-6

ment. A comparison of the stability of the complexes formed with Cu^{II} and Zn^{II}, the stereochemistries of which are known to be planar and tetrahedral, respectively, shows this effect. This is best illustrated in terms of the ligand replacement reaction (2-36) with different metal ions. At 20°C log K_R for

$$M(trien)^{+2} + tren \overset{K_R}{\rightleftharpoons} M(tren)^{+2} + trien \quad (2\text{-}36)$$

Cu is -1.6 and for Zn, 2.55. Thus Zn^{II} prefers *tren* to *trien*, while the reverse is true with Cu^{II}.

The number of chelate rings influences the stability of a complex, as shown by the trends in log K_1 (Table 2-4). Looking at this in a different way, using a replacement equilibrium (2-37), we see from the thermodynamic constants

$$[M(NH_3)_4]^{+2} + en \rightleftharpoons [M(NH_3)_2(en)]^{+2} + 2\,NH_3 \quad (2\text{-}37)$$

given in Table 2-5 that with Ni^{II} and Cu^{II} both the enthalpy and entropy contribute to stability while with Zn^{II}, it is entirely an entropy effect.

TABLE 2-4

Ligand	Number of rings	Co^{II}	Ni^{II}	Cu^{II}	Zn^{II}
en	1	6.0	7.9	10.8	6.0
den	2	8.1	10.7	16.0	8.9
trien	3	10.8	14.0	20.4	12.1
penten	5	15.8	19.3	22.4	16.2

TABLE 2-5

	$-\Delta G°$	$-\Delta H°$	$\Delta S°$
Ni^{II}	3.41	2.01	4.8
Cu^{II}	4.21	3.0	4.1
Zn^{II}	1.55	−0.1	5.3

The most favored ring size is the five-membered, although polynuclear complexes often contain four atoms in the ring and values of six and higher are sometimes obtained. Thus the impressions of preparative chemists have been confirmed by quantitative studies. Stability studies of dicarboxylic acids ($^-OOC(CH_2)_xCOO^-$) with Zn^{II}, Ni^{II}, and Cu^{II} have revealed similar trends to that of Mn^{II}:

ring size	5	6	7	8	10	12
$\log K_1$ (Mn^{II})	2.9	2.1	1.2	0.8	0.8	0.8

The coordination number of a metal ion may be changed by certain ligands. When this occurs, there is usually a change in the type of bonding. Nickel(II), for example, has a normal coordination number of six, found in complexes with water, most amines, halogens, and carboxylic acids, while with cyanide and dimethylglyoximate ions its C.N. drops to four. An interesting illustration of this is with the *C*-methyl substituted ethylenediamines (Table 2-6). In aqueous solu-

TABLE 2-6. Ni^{II} Complexes

N—C—C—N	C.N. = 6	N—C—C—N (with C, C above and C below)	C.N. = 4
N—C—C—N (with C above)	C.N. = 6	N—C—C—N (with C, C above and C, C below)	C.N. = 4
N—C—C—N (with C, C above)	C.N. = 4 or 6		

tion with excess diamine only the tri- and tetramethyl-ethylenediamines show a maximum C.N. of four. Associated with this change in C.N. are a change in color from the normal purple to yellow, a change in configuration (octahedral to planar), and a change in magnetic properties (paramagnetic to diamagnetic).

Unless steric factors are present, the logarithm of the ratio of successive constants is usually positive and roughly constant. With ethylenediamines, $\log K_1/K_2$ is usually 1.2–1.4; with ionic ligands, it is slightly larger. When steric factors are important, $\log K_1/K_2$ may be as large as 3 or 4. Negative values are known for a few systems such as Fe^{II}-dipy and o-phen. In these systems $K_1 > K_2 \ll K_3$. These reversals occur when a change in orbital hybridization takes place upon the addition of the final ligand.

Ligands which are able to accept negative charge or have resonance structures often form exceptionally stable complexes. In this way pyridine, although a very weak base, forms much stronger complexes with many transition metal ions than the strongly basic piperidine.

Metal Ion Effects. Several relationships governing the stability of complex ions are well established. In periodic groups Ia, IIa, and IIIa, the stability within each group increases as the size of the ion decreases and, between groups at nearly constant size, the stability increases with increasing charge. Thus, for several ligands, $Li^+ > Na^+ > K^+ > Rb^+ > Cs^+$, $Mg^{+2} > Ca^{+2} > Sr^{+2} > Ba^{+2} > Ra^{+2}$, and $Al^{+3} > Sc^{+3} > Y^{+3} > La^{+3}$. At essentially constant size, $Th^{+4} > Y^{+3} > Ca^{+2} > Na^+$ and $La^{+3} > Sr^{+2} > K^+$. For transition metal ions, however, large deviations often occur.

It has been shown with many different ligands under a variety of conditions that the stability of complexes follows a common order for +2 ions: $Pd > Cu > Ni > Co > Zn > Fe > Mn > Mg$. This is true regardless of the ligands involved or the type of atom coordinated (O, N, S, P). It has been pointed out that, as a first approximation, the stability decreases with increasing basicity of the metal.

In the first transition series, stability constant studies show a nonvarying pattern for K_1 and K_2 with most ligands and $+2$ metal ions (Fig. 2-7). Beyond manganese the constants increase with increasing atomic number, reaching a maximum with copper; a large decrease is observed with zinc. An analogous graph cannot be completed for $+3$ ions because of the instability of some of the metal ions in this oxidation state, but for those ions for which constants are available, a similar trend exists.

Figure 2-7

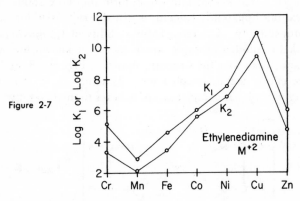

A similar curve is obtained for the heats of hydration of the metal ions, and thus the formation constant differences are probably directly related to the heats of formation of the complexes. The entropy changes remain nearly constant. On the basis of size and electronegativity, it would be expected that a nearly linear increase in heats of hydration or stability constants would occur with increasing atomic number. The maximum at Cu^{+2} has been explained on the basis of the *ligand field stabilization energy* (LFSE), which will be discussed in the chapter on bonding.

The above rules are upset if the ligand forms sufficiently

strong bonds which change the electronic configuration of the metal ion. For example, many complexes of iron(II) and nickel(II) with ligands such as cyanide ion and N-heterocyclic bases are much more stable than anticipated. In addition, certain ligands seem to be rather specific for a particular ion or group of ions. Apparently, the physical and chemical properties of a ligand may be "just right" to produce a complex of maximum stability with one ion while ions to either side in the periodic table would be somewhat mismatched. For example, EDTA complexes with Ca^{+2} are more stable than those with Mg^{+2}, Sr^{+2}, or Ba^{+2}. It would be expected that magnesium would form the more stable complex, but apparently calcium is just the right size for maximum stability. The remarkable stability of 1,2-dioximes for nickel is another example which has been known for many years. They have the structure shown in Figure 2-8, and the size of the metal, coupled with its tendency to form diamagnetic planar complexes, contributes to their stability.

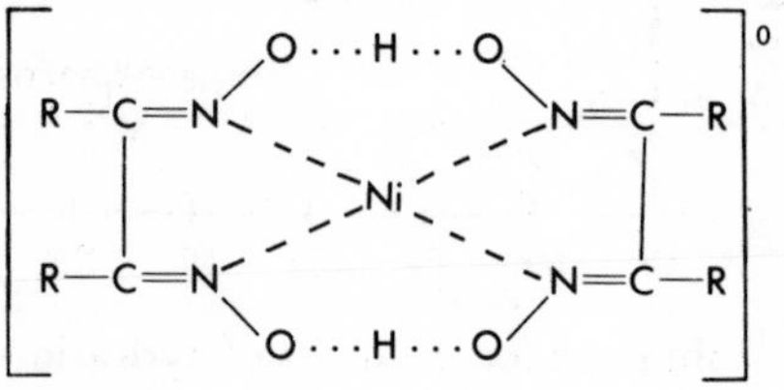

Figure 2-8

Stereochemical factors are also important as has been previously pointed out. Taking copper as an example, K_3 with ethylenediamine is extremely small compared to that for Ni^{II} or Zn^{II}. This is due to the reluctance of Cu^{II} to expand its coordination number to six.

Solvent Effects. Since stability constants pertain to reactions in which coordinated solvent is replaced by a new ligand, they are sensitive to the coordinating tendencies of the solvent. With solvents of low coordinating strength and in the absence of water, only a small amount of energy is lost in removing the coordinated solvent molecules. The energy of ligand association is about the same as in water, and thus the energy of the overall reaction is often considerably greater in noncoordinating solvents. In solvent mixtures, such as alcohol–water, the formation constant varies in an unpredictable manner. Often it rises to a maximum and then drops as the organic solvent is increased.

Heats of Reaction. The amount of heat involved in the formation of a complex is an important characteristic of the system. It is closely related to the difference between the strength of bonding of the incoming ligand and that of the solvent molecules being replaced. Often, in similar systems, the free energy change parallels the heat changes. A comparison of two unlike systems frequently shows large entropy change differences which are reflected in the free energy changes. In some cases this effect may be large enough so that the heat of a reaction may be smaller and yet the formation constant larger than in another system. Unfortunately, few precise heats of reaction are known because they usually must be measured in dilute solution where the temperature changes are small. With the recent availability of thermistors, sensitive temperature-measuring devices have been made and work in this field is proceeding at a rapid pace.

It is usually assumed that $\Delta H°$ is constant over a small range of temperature (50°), but this is never exactly true and sometimes is completely incorrect. Even in the acid dissociation of simple organic carboxylic acids, $\Delta H°$ varies considerably in a 25° temperature range. Although most work is reported at approximately room temperature, future work will probably report $\Delta H°$ over a range of temperatures and will be of somewhat greater value.

There are two useful methods of determining $\Delta H°$: (a) from the variation of $\Delta G°$ with temperature and (b) from direct or indirect calorimetry.

a. The change in $\ln K_F$ with temperature is related to the enthalpy change, $\Delta H°$, by the expression 2-8 on page 28. One usually determines $\ln K$ at several temperatures in the range 0–50°, and a graph of $\ln K$ versus $1/T$ gives a straight line whose slope is $-\Delta H°/R$. Of course, the line may be curved, in which case $\Delta H°$ is not constant and only an approximation may be made. In principle this method is convenient, but in practice it is inaccurate and is seldom used at the present time. The inaccuracies stem from the short range of temperatures which are accessible and the small changes in $\ln K$ which are observed. For a 10° change in temperature and a $\Delta H°$ of 10 kcal/mole, $\Delta \ln K$ is about 0.5. Since the precision of $\ln K$ is usually about ± 0.1, the enthalpy changes are usually unreliable.

b. For accurate $\Delta H°$ measurements, direct calorimetry is preferred. Many calorimeters are available, but probably the most sensitive and versatile uses a thermistor as the temperature-sensing device. In practice, a known amount of metal ion solution is added to a stirred solution containing excess ligand, and temperature rise of the mixture is measured. From the amount of complex formed, the heat capacity of the final mixture, and the temperature rise, $\Delta H°$ may be evaluated. Figure 2-9 shows a diagram of one type of calorimeter presently in use. For most complexes in about $10^{-2} M$ concentration, the temperature rise is of the order of 0.02°. This must be corrected for the heat of dilution of the metal ion (often very small), and for the heat involved in the pH change which may occur. This is easily done, however, and $\Delta H°$ can easily be measured to ± 0.05 kcal/mole.

There are certain situations which may cause some difficulty. It may not be possible to set conditions such that the metal ion is completely converted to the complex, and then it is necessary to know from some other source how much is formed. This may be determined from the formation constants or by direct spectrophotometric measurements. When

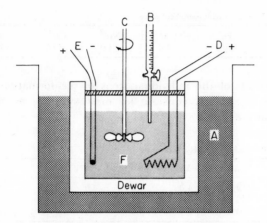

Figure 2-9. Calorimeter. A, Constant temperature bath. B, F, Reactant solutions. C, Low speed stirrer. D, Heater. E, Thermistor.

formation reactions are slow, the method is not applicable. In this case, indirect calorimetric measurements may be used, taking advantage of another reaction which is fast, such as complex decomposition.

In principle, the stepwise heats may be determined using the correct proportions of ligand and metal ion as determined from the formation constants. This is more difficult and is subject to greater error than the overall heats.

$\Delta H°$ is affected by the ionic environment. Thus the enthalpy change in $1M$ NaCl solution is not always the same as in $1M$ $NaClO_4$, nor are the values in $0.1M$ and $1M$ $NaClO_4$ the same. When $\Delta G°$ and $\Delta H°$ are to be related to obtain values for $\Delta S°$, it is usually necessary that they be determined in the same ionic medium.

In general, the enthalpy changes parallel the free energy changes because the entropy changes are nearly constant. Some first association heats, $-\Delta H°_1$, for trien are given in Table 2-7.

TABLE 2-7. $-\Delta H^\circ_1$ with trien, kcal/mole

Mn^{+2}	Fe^{+2}	Co^{+2}	Ni^{+2}	Cu^{+2}	Zn^{+2}
4.0	9.0	9.0	13.0	22.0	9.8

The heats of the individual steps of the formation of a complex are nearly constant for most systems, as shown by Table 2-8.

TABLE 2-8. $-\Delta H^\circ$ with NH_3, kcal/mole

	$-\Delta H^\circ_1$	$-\Delta H^\circ_2$	$-\Delta H^\circ_3$	$-\Delta H^\circ_4$	$-\Delta H^\circ_5$	$-\Delta H^\circ_6$
Ni^{II}	4.0	4.0	4.0	4.0	4.3	4.3
Cu^{II}	5.6	5.5	5.6	6.3		
Cd^{II}	3.5	3.5	3.5	3.5	3.5	3.5

TABLE 2-9. $-\Delta H^\circ$ with en, kcal/mole

	$-\Delta H^\circ_1$	$-\Delta H^\circ_2$	$-\Delta H^\circ_3$
Ni^{II}	9.01	9.18	9.71
Cu^{II}	13.0	12.4	Very small

In certain cases, where a lower coordination number is more stable, the last heat, $-\Delta H^\circ_3$, may be quite small. Such is the case with Cu^{II} (Table 2-9), which has little tendency to expand its coordination number to six. The largest effect on the heat comes from the type of ligand, and in general, the order of ligands is preserved from one metal ion to another. For Cu^{II} the order in Table 2-10 has been obtained, and other studies with the same donor atom show that the heats of a bidentate are nearly twice and a tridentate nearly three times that observed with a monodentate ligand.

Entropy Changes.   Using the relationship $\Delta G^\circ = \Delta H^\circ - T\Delta S^\circ$, we may determine the entropy change of a reaction from the measured ΔG° and ΔH°. Because it is a difference between two rather large numbers, ΔS° is often known with much less precision than the others. However, certain trends are apparent. Usually for monodentate ligands replacing coordinated water, $\Delta S°$ is nearly zero while polydentate ligands give positive values such as those listed in Table 2-11. The increased value of $\Delta S°$ with polydentate ligands is related to the increasing freedom of the system because of the release of water molecules, giving an increase in the number of particles in the products. Consider reactions 2-38 and 2-39.

$$[Ni(H_2O)_6]^{+2} + NH_3 \rightarrow [Ni(NH_3)(H_2O)_5]^{+2} + H_2O \quad (2\text{-}38)$$

$$[Ni(H_2O)_6]^{+2} + en \rightarrow [Ni(en)(H_2O)_4]^{+2} + 2\,H_2O \quad (2\text{-}39)$$

The major difference between them is in the number of water molecules released. In reaction 2-38, for every water molecule released, one NH_3 molecule is bound and thus the freedom of rotation lost by an NH_3 molecule is gained by an H_2O molecule. Since both are of the same order of magnitude, no net change in entropy is observed. On the other hand, reaction 2-39 gives two water molecules for every ethylenediamine coordinated, and freedom gained by them is not completely compensated for by the loss of freedom of the ethylenediamine molecule. Thus an entropy change is found, and it is positive and contributes to the free energy. An increase in randomness of a system results in a positive $\Delta S°$ which adds to a negative $\Delta H°$ to give a more negative $\Delta G°$. Further, the more negative $\Delta G°$, the larger the formation constant, so an increase in randomness causes greater complex stability.

TABLE 2-10.
$-\Delta H°_1$ with Cu^{II}, kcal/mole

acac	4.7
NH_3	5.6
EDTA	8.67
en	13.0
trien	22.0

TABLE 2-11

Metal	Ligand	$\Delta S°$
Ni^{II}	2(en)	3.4
Cu^{II}	2(en)	7.1
Zn^{II}	2(en)	7.6
Ni^{II}	EDTA	56.7
Cu^{II}	EDTA	56.4
Zn^{II}	EDTA	56.3

chapter three

REACTION SPEEDS

So FAR we have described two aspects of complex formation reactions: the nature of the reactants and products and the quantitative aspects of the equilibria (K_F, $\Delta G°$, $\Delta H°$, and $\Delta S°$). The first of these tells us what can be produced; the second indicates the extent to which the reaction will proceed at equilibrium. Neither tells us, however, if the reaction will proceed in a measurable length of time. A complete description of a system requires a quantitative determination of the speed of reaction. This aspect is called *kinetics*, and, although little emphasis has been placed on it until recent years, it is as important as the thermodynamic quantities.

In order for reactants to proceed to products, two conditions must be fulfilled: (a) ΔG must be negative—that is, the experimental conditions must be such that, at equilibrium, products will be present in appreciable amounts—and (b) a reaction path must be available under the conditions of the experiment. Consider the reaction:

$$8\,H^+ + ClO_4^- + 8\,Cr^{+2} \rightleftharpoons Cl^- + 8\,Cr^{+3} + 4\,H_2O \quad (3\text{-}1)$$

for which $\Delta G° = -41.$ kcal/equiv. At equilibrium (after many months) only a very small concentration of reactants are present. However, experiment shows that in the reaction of Cr^{+2} with ClO_4^- little Cr^{+3} or Cl^- is discernible during the first few days of reaction. Although the free energy change is favorable, a low energy reaction path is not available.

By studying the kinetics of many reactions, chemists hope

to be able to predict which reactions will proceed rapidly and which will be slow. At the present time qualitative predictions are usually correct, but a quantitative prediction is not reliable.

Another value of kinetic measurements is the establishment of the mechanism of the reaction. The mechanism involves two parts: the reactions preceding the formation of the activated complex and those following it. Very often two molecules or ions do not react directly; one or more intermediates may be involved. Thus the reaction of A with B to give C may take place through the intermediates d, e, and f according to these hypothetical equations:

$$A \rightarrow d \qquad d + e \rightarrow \lceil de \rceil \rightarrow f \qquad f \rightarrow C \qquad (3\text{-}2)$$
$$B \rightarrow e$$

The intermediates are often not isolable and exist in such small concentrations during reaction that their presence may not be demonstrated by physical or chemical means. Likewise the activated complex $\lceil de \rceil$ usually can exist for only very short periods of time (microseconds). The rate expression for the reaction $A + B \rightarrow C$ is dependent on the composition of the activated state and can provide a great deal of information about the intermediates (d or e) in favorable cases.

Rate Measurement

The rate of reaction is the amount of reactant lost or the amount of product formed per unit time. Generally, for reactions conducted in solution, the amount is given in moles per liter and the time in minutes or seconds. The rate of reaction is not constant but varies with concentration, temperature, solvent, and, to a lesser extent, with pressure. First we will consider the determination of a rate of reaction at constant temperature and pressure and in the solvent water. Later, the effect of varying these factors will be discussed.

Suppose we wish to measure the rate of isomerization of a nitrito complex to the nitro form. The reaction (3-3) may be visualized as proceeding from reactant through activated state to product. The energy requirements of such a system

$$[(NH_3)_5Co-O-N-O]^{+2} \rightarrow \left[(NH_3)_5-Co\leftarrow\overset{\nearrow O}{\underset{|}{N}}-O \right]^{+2} \rightarrow$$

Orange

$$[(NH_3)_5Co-NO_2]^{+2} \quad (3-3)$$

Yellow

are pictured in Figure 3-1. As can be seen, the energy of a reactant molecule has to be raised to that of the activated state before the reaction can occur. When the products are formed from the activated state, energy E_b is released, so that there is a net evolution of energy, E_r. It is not possible to go directly from reactants to products, and of all the reactant

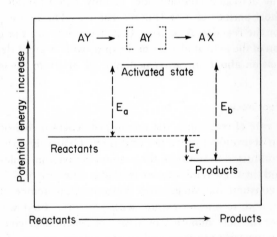

Figure 3-1. Energy Diagram of Reaction Illustrating the Energy of Activation.

molecules, only a certain small percentage possess enough energy to pass through the activated state and these are converted directly to product. These higher energy molecules are constantly being replaced by molecular collisions, and thus the percentage of high energy molecules remains constant. The rate at which product molecules are formed is determined by the number of molecules which acquire enough energy to reach the activated state; at constant temperature this is proportional to the total number of reactant molecules or the number of moles per unit volume. In equation form, rate $= k[(NH_3)_5Co\text{—}ONO^{+2}]$, where k is the rate constant. During a reaction the rate will not remain constant, because the number of reactant molecules decreases as the product forms. Since the rate equals $-d[(NH_3)_5Co\text{—}ONO^{+2}]/dt$,

$$-d[(NH_3)_5Co\text{—}ONO^{+2}]/dt = k[(NH_3)_5Co\text{—}ONO^{+2}] \quad (3\text{-}4)$$

or

$$-d[(NH_3)_5Co\text{—}ONO^{+2}]/[(NH_3)_5Co\text{—}ONO^{+2}] = kdt \quad (3\text{-}5)$$

and

$$-\int_{t=0}^{t=t} d[(NH_3)_5Co\text{—}ONO^{+2}]/[(NH_3)_5Co\text{—}ONO^{+2}] = \int_{t=0}^{t=t} kdt \quad (3\text{-}6)$$

which gives

$$\ln\{[(NH_3)_5Co\text{—}ONO^{+2}]_0/[(NH_3)_5Co\text{—}ONO^{+2}]_t\}$$
$$= k(t - t_0) = kt \quad (3\text{-}7)$$

Thus a graph of the left-hand term versus t will give a straight line whose slope equals the rate constant, k.

Any technique which measures the concentration of one of the reactants or one of the products may be used to determine the kinetics of a reaction. For accurate results many points on the concentration-versus-time curve are necessary, so that the technique should be rapid as well as accurate.

For this reason spectrophotometric methods and volumetric titrations are often used.

Many other methods have been used to study reaction kinetics. Most depend on a change in a physical property during reaction. In addition to those discussed here, optical activity, pressure measurements for gaseous reactions, volume changes (dilatometry) in solution, refractometry, potentiometry, polarography, thermal conductivity, viscosity changes, and heats of reaction have been utilized.

Spectrophotometric Methods. Since most complexes are highly colored and the color is sensitive to changes in the coordinated ligands, absorption spectroscopy is probably the most valuable tool for rate determinations. For example, the acid decomposition of $[Ni(tetrameen)_2]^{+2}$ can easily be followed because the complex has a strong absorption band at about 420 mμ while the products, $[Ni(H_2O)_x]^{+2}$ and $[tetrameen-H_2]^{+2}$, are colorless in this region.

Titrimetric Methods. Volumetric titrations are often employed for reactions of type 3-8. The halide ion

$$[Co(NH_3)_5Cl]^{+2} + H_2O \rightarrow [Co(NH_3)_5OH_2]^{+3} + Cl^- \quad (3\text{-}8)$$

liberated by reaction may be titrated with $Hg(NO_3)_2$ to produce $HgCl_2$, which is essentially unionized, and if the titration is properly conducted, the coordinated halide ion is not removed from the complex by Hg^{+2}. In an analogous manner, acid-base titrations may be used to determine the rate of reaction 3-8. The aquo complex produced is a weak acid due to equilibrium 3-9. Since the chloro complex does not

$$[Co(NH_3)_5OH_2]^{+3} \rightleftharpoons [Co(NH_3)_5OH]^{+2} + H^+_{aq} \quad (3\text{-}9)$$

have acidic properties, the amount of aquo complex may be determined by titration with OH^- using a suitable indicator.

Conductimetric Methods. Measurement of the variation in electrical conductivity of a complex solution is an excellent method of determining rates of reaction because it can be used at extremely low concentrations. It is especially valuable and sensitive when one of the reactants or products is nonionic. The reaction of $[Pt(en)(NO_2)H_2O]^+$ with NO_2^- to give $[Pt(en)(NO_2)_2]^0$ shows a large decrease in conductivity.

Isotopic Methods. Both radioactive and nonradioactive isotopes are applicable to rate studies. They may be used in two ways: (a) to determine the amount of a reactant or product present in solution by isotopic dilution and (b) to determine the rate of isotopic exchange.

a. Isotopic dilution. Using the radioactive isotope Cl^{36}, one can measure the concentration of free Cl^- at any time which is formed by reaction 3-10. After the reaction has proceeded

$$[Pt(NH_3)_5Cl]^{+3} + H_2O \rightarrow [Pt(NH_3)_5OH_2]^{+4} + Cl^- \quad (3\text{-}10)$$

for a measured time, a known amount of radioactive chloride ion is added. This is followed by addition of Ag^+, which immediately precipitates all of the *free* chloride ion (both radioactive and nonradioactive) as AgCl. The amount of radioactivity per unit weight of AgCl is determined, and this is related to the free Cl^- which was present in solution by a simple equation. This method is slow and not always of the highest precision, but is often useful when other methods fail. Stable isotopes such as O^{18} or N^{15} may also be used and the measurement of the isotopic abundance determined with a mass spectrometer.

b. Isotopic exchange. Suppose that we wish to know how fast a complex exchanges its ligands for identical ligands present in solution. Such an exchange would be typified by reaction 3-11. Since there is no net change in the concentra-

$$[Fe(CN)_6]^{-3} + \overset{*}{C}N^- \rightleftharpoons [Fe(\overset{*}{C}N)_6]^{-3} + CN^- \quad (3\text{-}11)$$

tions of the reactants, isotopic exchange reactions cannot be followed by chemical methods. Using either radioactive or stable isotopes the rate can be determined. If cyanide ion containing some radioactive C^{14} is added to a solution of normal $[Fe(CN)_6]^{-3}$ the radioactivity will be found to in- crease gradually in the $[Fe(CN)_6]^{-3}$. This ion may be pre- cipitated at various time intervals and its radioactivity meas- ured. From this the rate of exchange may be calculated. Of course, the reaction does not go to completion and ulti- mately results in an equal distribution of radioactivity be- tween the CN^- and the $[Fe(CN)_6]^{-3}$. A correction for this must be made in evaluating the rate constant.

An interesting exchange reaction involves the rate of water exchange with solvent water, as illustrated in equation 3-12. (Since there is no useful radioactive isotope of oxygen this was studied with the stable isotope O^{18}.) O^{18}-enriched water

$$[Cr(H_2O)_6]^{+3} \ + \ H_2\overset{*}{O} \ \rightarrow \ [Cr(H_2\overset{*}{O})_6]^{+3} \ + \ H_2O \qquad (3\text{-}12)$$

was added to "normal" $[Cr(H_2O)_6]^{+3}$. The isotopic composi- tion of the water in $[Cr(H_2O)_6]^{+3}$ was determined as a func- tion of time, and from this the rate constant was obtained.

Form of the Rate Expression

In solution reactions, the rate is usually a *simple* function of the reactant concentrations. For the reaction A $\rightarrow$ prod- ucts, the rate expression can usually be expected to be of the form: rate $= k[A]^n$, where n ordinarily has a value of 1, 2, or 3. There are several methods by which the value of n may be determined experimentally. The trial and error method is often used; this involves guessing the value of n and applying it to the experimental changes of [A] with time to see if appropriate values are obtained. If $n = 1$, rate $= -d[A]/dt = k[A]$, or $-d[A]/[A] = kdt$, or $\ln [A]_0/[A] = kt$. A graph of $-\ln [A]$ versus t will be a straight line if the reaction is first order in [A]. If $n = 2$, $-d[A]/dt = k[A]^2$, or $-d[A]/[A]^2 = kdt$, or $1/[A] - 1/[A_0] = kt$, and a graph of $(1/[A] - 1/[A_0])$ versus t will be a straight line. If the reaction is followed to only 10–20% completion, a straight line will usually be ap- proximated by all the equations ($n = 1, 2, 3$), and thus a wise experimenter is careful to use at least 90% of the complete reaction to evaluate the order with respect to a reactant.

When a reaction involves more than one reactant (3-13),

$$A + B \rightarrow products \qquad (3\text{-}13)$$

the rate expression often becomes: rate $= k[A]^n[B]^m$. Although the equations relating [A], [B], k, and t can usually be evaluated for various combinations of n and m values, and then tested by trial and error with the experimental data, a more common method involves "swamping" the reaction with one reactant and determining the order with respect to the other.

If [B] is more than 1000 times greater than [A], the concentration of B will not change during the reaction. The reaction is then dependent on the general expression: rate $= k[B]^m[A]^n$, or rate $= k'[A]^n$. The reaction behaves as if it is only dependent on [A]. The value of n may be determined by graphical methods as in the simple one-reactant case. Then, by reversing the procedure and "swamping" the system with A, the value of m may be found. If $n = 1$ in the presence of a large excess of B, the reaction is said to be pseudo first order; if $n = 2$, it is pseudo second order in A.

From the foregoing it must not be assumed that reactions are usually simple kinetically. More often than not complicating factors are involved which are subject to interpretation. In many cases fractional values of n emerge because of equilibria preceding the activated state; n may be negative in certain cases; and sometimes the products appear in the rate expression. Another frequent complication is the ionic strength effect, which ordinarily manifests itself in non-integral values of n. The skilled experimenter is usually able to anticipate these effects and is often able to design his experiments so that these factors can be evaluated separately, allowing a clear evaluation of the basic kinetic equation. When this is done, rate expressions for the individual steps usually are relatively simple and without fractional or non-integral exponents.

Unfortunately, however, the rate expression as determined above may not be complete and may be subject to certain ambiguities. The role of the solvent is not included and, as is well known, the solvent has a strong effect on the rate of reaction. Most inorganic reactions are speeded up in the presence of a solvent having a high dielectric constant. The order with respect to solvent is usually difficult or impossible to determine. In the reaction of $[Co(NH_3)_5Br]^{+2}$ with H_2O to give $[Co(NH_3)_5OH_2]^{+3}$ and Br^-, the rate is first order in $[Co(NH_3)_5Br]^{+2}$; but, since the water is always present in large excess, its order cannot be determined. Theoretically, it should be possible to lower the H_2O concentration by using another solvent which does not react (such as an alcohol). This procedure, however, is complicated by ion-pair formation and alcohol-H_2O interaction, and does not lead to a useful value for the order with respect to H_2O.

Another factor which should be pointed out is the possibility that the reactant species is not the one which appears in the rate expression. For an example let us consider the reaction of a hydrated metal ion with a chloride ion:

$$[M(H_2O)_6]^{+2} \quad + \quad Cl^- \quad \rightarrow \quad [M(H_2O)_5Cl]^+ \quad + \quad H_2O \quad (3\text{-}14)$$

A kinetic study made in H_2O might show the rate expression to be: rate $= k[M(H_2O)_6^{+2}][Cl^-]$, whereas the correct rate expression may be: rate $= k[M(H_2O)_5OH^+][Cl^-]$. This possibility comes about because of the equilibrium

$$[M(H_2O)_6]^{+2} \quad \rightleftharpoons \quad [M(H_2O)_5OH]^+ \quad + \quad H^+_{aq} \quad (3\text{-}15)$$

Thus, at constant pH, there will exist a direct relationship between $[M(H_2O)_6^{+2}]$ and $[M(H_2O)_5OH^+]$ and either complex could be the reacting species. Which of the two rate expressions is correct could be found in this case by determining the pH dependence of the rate. Qualitatively, if the rate is independent of [OH⁻], then $[M(H_2O)_6]^{+2}$ is the reacting species, while an increase in rate with increasing [OH⁻] strongly suggests $[M(H_2O)_5OH]^+$ as the reactant.

It has been known for many years that a temperature rise causes an increase in reaction rate. A rough generalization for solution reactions is that the rate increases by a factor of two for a 10° temperature rise. The relationship between temperature and rate is often expressed in terms of the Arrhenius equation:

$$\ln k \;=\; \ln A \;-\; E_a/RT \tag{3-16}$$

where k is the rate constant; E_a is the activation energy, which is positive when going from reactants to the activated state; and A is the frequency factor, which may be thought of as the product of the rate of collision and the relative effectiveness of each collision. From this equation a graph of $\ln k$ versus $1/T$ should be a straight line with slope $-E_a/R$ and with an intercept of $\ln A$. Over a limited temperature range (50°) most solution reactions follow this equation.

The physical significance of A and E_a values is difficult to assess. The magnitude of E_a reflects the amount of organization of bond distances and angles of the activated state as compared to those of the reactants.

A reaction conducted at high pressure will have a slightly different rate than at atmospheric pressure. An activated state having a smaller volume than the sum of the volumes of the reactants will form more rapidly when the pressure is high. The change in rate with changes in pressure is so small that it is neglected in ordinary studies, but it is useful when information about the relative volume of the activated state is desired.

Often the rate expression contains several terms which describe separate paths by which the reaction occurs. For instance, in the exchange of Cl⁻ with AuCl₄⁻, which was followed by using radioactive chloride ion, the kinetic expression took the form:

$$\text{rate} = k_1[\text{AuCl}_4^-] + k_2[\text{AuCl}_4^-][\text{Cl}^-] \qquad (3\text{-}17)$$

If we neglect the solvent interaction, the first term can be thought of as a reversible dissociation causing exchange 3-18

$$\text{AuCl}_4^- \rightleftharpoons \text{AuCl}_3 + \text{Cl}^-$$

$$\text{AuCl}_3 + \overset{*}{\text{Cl}}^- \rightleftharpoons \text{AuCl}_3\overset{*}{\text{Cl}}^- \qquad (3\text{-}18)$$

AuCl_3 has a very low stability and is expected to be present in only minute amounts, but, because of solvent interaction, it is present in high enough concentration to permit this part of the exchange.

The second term of 3-17 relates to another path by which the exchange occurs. In this case the activated state involves an AuCl_4^- and a Cl^-. In a broad sense the incoming Cl^- displaces one of the coordinated chloride ions. Thus it is called displacement mechanism. In the actual exchange reaction both dissociation and displacement mechanisms operate simultaneously, although one path usually dominates.

From the foregoing it can be seen that the contents of the rate expression for each individual path are closely related to the actual species involved in the activated state. Thus a mechanistic picture of how the reaction occurs may be deduced from the form of the rate expression.

Coordination chemists often describe a reaction according to the form of the rate expression. The terminology stems from that developed and used in the organic field. Two types of substitution are generally recognized: nucleophilic substitution, S_N, and electrophilic substitution, S_E. A nucleophilic substance tends to donate electrons to an atom (3-19) while an electrophilic reagent tends to remove electrons from another atom (3-20) (M and M' are metal ions, Y and X ligands).

$$\text{Y:} + \text{M—X} \rightarrow \text{M—Y} + \text{X:} \qquad S_N \qquad (3\text{-}19)$$

$$\text{M'} + \text{M—X:} \rightleftharpoons \text{M'—X:} + \text{M} \qquad S_E \qquad (3\text{-}20)$$

In coordination chemistry ligands are nucleophilic reagents and metal ions are electrophilic reagents. A further extension of this description includes the form of the kinetic rate expression. If it has only one term to the first power, it it called an S_N1 or S_E1 reaction, while if it contains two terms to the first power it is S_N2 or S_E2.* As an example consider the S_N reaction 3-21. If the rate expression is: rate =

$$[Fe(H_2O)_6]^{+3} + Cl^- \rightleftharpoons [Fe(H_2O)_5Cl]^{+2} + H_2O \quad (3\text{-}21)$$

$k[Fe(H_2O)_6^{+3}]$, then it is of the S_N1 type, while if the rate expression is: rate = $k[Fe(H_2O_6^{+3}][Cl^-]$, it would be of the S_N2 type. Of course in reactions where more than one path is operative the reaction may be both S_N1 and S_N2.

With few exceptions the rate constants for the forward and reverse steps of a reaction are directly related to the equilibrium constant for that reaction. Consider the general reaction 3-22, having a rate constant of formation k_F, and the reverse reaction 3-23, having a rate constant of decomposition of k_D. The rates will be described by the expressions

$$M^{+2} + 4A \rightarrow MA_4^{+2} \quad (3\text{-}22)$$

$$MA_4^{+2} \rightarrow M^{+2} + 4A \quad (3\text{-}23)$$

$$\text{rate of formation} = k_F[M^{+2}][A]^4$$

$$\text{rate of decomposition} = k_D[MA_4^{+2}] \quad (3\text{-}24)$$

At equilibrium the rate of formation must equal the rate of decomposition and thus

$$k_F[M^{+2}][A^4] = k_D[MA_4^{+2}] \quad (3\text{-}25)$$

Rearranging gives

$$k_F/k_D = [MA_4^{+2}]/[M^{+2}][A]^4 \quad (3\text{-}26)$$

But $$K_{eq} = [MA_4^{+2}]/[M^{+2}][A]^4 \quad (3\text{-}27)$$

and so $$k_F/k_D = K_{eq} \quad (3\text{-}28)$$

*More accurately, these terms refer to the number of reactants comprising the activated state.

chapter four

MODE OF BONDING

IT WAS NOTICED early that there was a close similarity between the covalent bond in organic chemistry and the coordinate bond in inorganic complexes. Following the theory of Lewis and Sidgwick on electron-pair bonding, it seemed reasonable that ligands donate electron pairs to metal ions, thus forming the coordinate link. This approach was extended by L. Pauling into the *valence bond theory*, which was quite successful in describing and predicting much of the magnetic behavior, stereochemistry, kinetics, and other chemical and physical properties known in the 1930's and next two decades. Toward the end of the 1950's certain facts became known which were not easily explainable by this theory, and the *electrostatic field theory* (also known as the *crystal field theory*) and the *ligand field theory* were revived from the early work of J. H. Van Vleck and H. Bethe. These theories were found to be somewhat more valuable for describing metal-ligand interaction, and were especially helpful in explaining the visible absorption spectra of the complexes.

Also during the years since 1935 the *molecular orbital theory* was being developed, and its application to simple highly covalent species has been particularly fruitful. In principle this is the most exact theory, but, since calculations and predictions are made only with great difficulty, the other three are generally used in relation to complex bonding.

Valence Bond Theory

A metal ion coordination compound forms by a process

similar to the addition of a hydrogen ion to an ammonia molecule (4-1). The ammonia molecule has a pair of unshared electrons which are shared with the metal ion (H^+ in

$$H^+ \quad + \quad :NH_3 \quad \rightarrow \quad [H:NH_3]^+ \qquad (4\text{-}1)$$

Metal   Ligand   Complex
ion

this case) to form a bond. All of the hydrogens are equivalent in the ammonium ion because of the equivalence of the four sp^3 hybrid orbitals.

When metal ions are used in place of H^+, the number of NH_3 molecules which may be attached is usually more than one (4-2 and 4-3), but the bonding may be considered to be of

$$Ag^+ \quad + \quad 2:NH_3 \quad \rightarrow \quad [Ag(:NH_3)_2]^+ \qquad (4\text{-}2)$$

$$Cu^{+2} \quad + \quad 4:NH_3 \quad \rightarrow \quad [Cu(:NH_3)_4]^{+2} \qquad (4\text{-}3)$$

essentially the same type. According to the *valence bond theory* the association results from overlap of an orbital of the ligand containing an unshared pair of electrons with hybridized orbitals of the metal ion. This may be thought of either as a sharing of the electron pair between the metal ion and ligand or as a partial donation of the ligand electrons to the metal ion.

From the standpoint of depicting the bonding in terms of the electron configuration of the metal ion, it is profitable to consider that the ligand electron pairs enter the metal ion orbitals while still maintaining the electronic configuration originally present in the ligand.

If we consider the formation of the ion $[AlCl_4]^-$ each chloride ion donates a pair of electrons to the Al^{+3}. This can be visualized in the manner of Figure 4-1. Each chloride ion retains its electronic configuration ($1s^2 2s^2 2p^6 3s^2 3p^6$). One chloride ion would be expected to be bound differently than the rest since it uses an s orbital of the metal, but this is not found experimentally. In order to overcome this diffi-

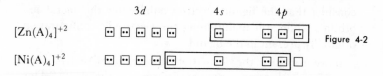

		3s		3p		
Al^{+3}	$(1s^2 2s^2 2p^6)$	□		□ □ □		Figure 4-1
AlCl$_4$$^-$	$(1s^2 2s^2 2p^6 3s^2 3p^6)$	⊡		⊡ ⊡ ⊡		

culty the four metal orbitals involved are thought to interact in such a way as to produce four equivalent orbitals (four sp^3 orbitals), a process called *hybridization*. The hybridized orbitals have definite directional characteristics dependent primarily on the metal ion. Thus any complex containing sp^3 hybridization would have the bonds, and therefore the ligands, directed in space, in the present case toward the corners of a tetrahedron.

Numerous combinations of s, p, and d orbitals are possible, giving rise to hybridized orbitals of different spatial geometry. In practice, however, only a small number are encountered in metal complexes (Table 4-1). The type of hybridization and thus the spatial arrangement of the ligands depend on several factors, the most important of which is the number of d electrons in the free metal ion. Thus a d^{10} ion such as Zn^{+2} prefers sp^3 hybridization, while a d^8 ion such as Ni^{+2} prefers dsp^2 hybridization (Fig. 4-2). Both the coordination number and the geometric configuration of a complex ion are dependent to some extent on the properties of the ligand.

Figure 4-2

For instance Ni^{+2}, a d^8 ion, may take the configurations in Figure 4-3. In general, however, a metal ion in a particular oxidation state retains a fixed coordination number and configuration in most of its complexes. A partial list of common configuration is given in Table 4-1 as a guide.

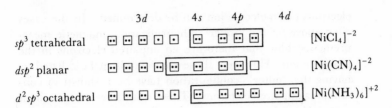

Figure 4-3

TABLE 4-1

Configuration	Ions
sp or dp (linear)	Ag^+, Hg^{+2}
sp^3 (tetrahedral)	Al^{+3}, Zn^{+2}, Ni^{+2} (on rare occasions), Co^{+2}, Ti^{+3}, Fe^{+2}
dsp^2 (planar)	Pt^{+2}, Pd^{+2}, Ag^{+2}, Cu^{+2}, Ni^{+2}, Au^{+3}
d^2sp^3 (octahedral)	Cr^{+3}, Co^{+3}, Ni^{+2}, Pd^{+4}, Pt^{+4}, Mn^{+3}, Re^{+4}

With certain metals in the first transition group, the possibility exists of using either $3d$ or $4d$ orbitals for hybridization. Take the Fe^{+2} ion (d^6) as an example (Fig. 4-4). The first configuration is taken in the complexes $[Fe(o\text{-phen})_3]^{+2}$ and $[Fe(CN)_6]^{-4}$, while the outer sphere configuration is taken in the complexes $[Fe(NH_3)_6]^{+2}$ and $[Fe(en)_3]^{+2}$. Much of the evidence for assignment of these configurations comes from studies on the magnetic behavior of the complexes. Substances which have unpaired electrons are paramagnetic, while substances in which all of the electrons are paired are diamagnetic. This magnetism can be simply and accurately measured and, from its magnitude, the number of unpaired

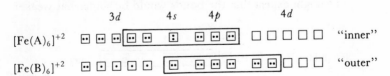

Figure 4-4

electrons per molecule ion can be determined. In the cases cited above for the "inner" *d* hybridization, magnetic measurements show that there are no unpaired electrons in the molecule ion. However, those compounds of Fe^{+2} listed as having the "outer" configuration have been shown to contain four unpaired electrons. These results are in agreement with and tend to substantiate the diagrammatic description given in Figure 4-4.

The valence bond theory has proved remarkably successful for predicting qualitatively the rate at which ligand exchange occurs, and the descriptive terms *labile* and *inert* have come into common usage. A complex which is labile readily reacts with substances capable of replacing the attached ligand, while inert complexes are sluggish in similar reactions. A comparison of the rates of reaction of $[Fe(CN)_6]^{-4}$ ("inner" *d* hybridization) and $[Fe(NH_3)_6]^{+2}$ ("outer" *d* hybridization) with acids shows that the former reacts very slowly while the latter reacts instantaneously. The same is true with most other reagents which ultimately cause the decomposition of both complexes. A careful consideration of many complexes led to recognition of two conditions, either of which give rise to lability: (1) the use of "outer" *d* hybridization and (2) the presence of one or more completely empty "inner" *d* orbitals. The behavior of Fe^{+2} illustrates the first, while a comparison of $[V(NH_3)_6]^{+3}$ and $[Cr(NH_3)_6]^{+3}$ (Fig. 4-5) provides an illustration of the latter. Both of these conditions seem plausible in the light of possible reaction mechanisms.

In species which are coordinated using "outer" *d* orbitals, one might expect that the bonds would be somewhat weaker

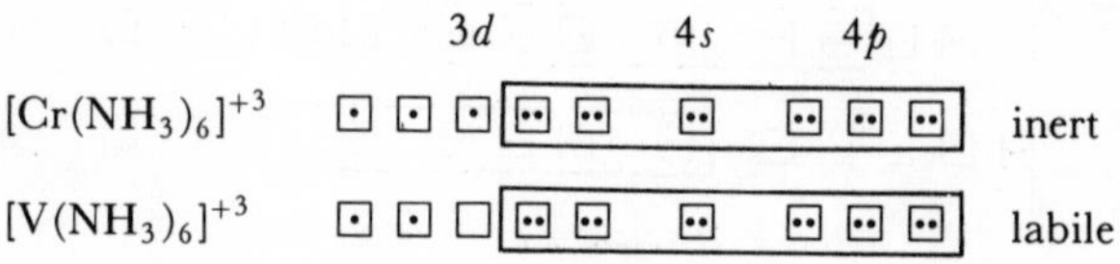

Figure 4-5

than those in complexes using "inner" d orbitals. The weakness of the bonds would tend to allow dissociation of one group from the complex, leading to replacement of that group (4-4). A complex containing a completely vacant

$$Y_5M-X \xrightarrow{-X} Y_5M \xrightarrow{Z} Y_5M-Z \qquad (4\text{-}4)$$

"inner" d orbital would have some tendency to increase its coordination number by coordinating an additional group. Rearrangement and expulsion of one of the original ligands would complete the exchange (4-5). In those cases where

$$Y_5M-X \ + \ Z \ \rightarrow \ Y_5-M\diagdown^{X}_{Z} \ \rightarrow \ Y_5-M-Z \ + \ X \qquad (4\text{-}5)$$

neither of these conditions are satisfied, considerable energy must be supplied to provide a path for the reaction, thus making the reaction a great deal slower by comparison.

The valence bond theory has been reasonably successful in explaining the bonding in coordination compounds, but it has not allowed quantitative predictions to be made.

Electrostatic Field Theory

This approach was first applied to solid ionic type crystalline substances and so is often called the *crystal field theory*. Whereas the valence bond theory assumed that ligand electrons are partially donated to metal orbitals, the electrostatic field theory considers the bonding to be entirely electrostatic, an attraction between a positively charged metal ion and the partial negative charge invariably present on the ligands. In its pure state the electrostatic field theory does not provide for ligand electrons to enter the metal orbitals. The chemical and physical properties of the complex depend to a large extent on the modifications, produced by the ligands, in the energy levels of the metal ion d orbitals. Let us start, then, by looking at drawings of the calculated distribution of elec-

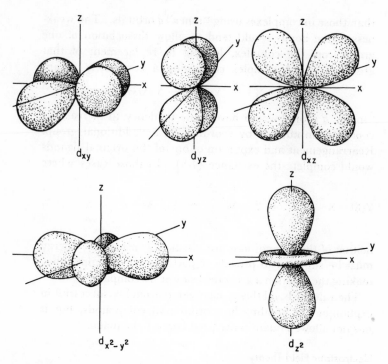

Figure 4-6. Conventional Boundary Surfaces of the *d* Atomic Orbitals. (From M. C. Day, Jr., and J. Selbin, "Theoretical Inorganic Chemistry," Reinhold, New York, 1962)

tron density in the five *d* orbitals of a transition metal ion (Fig. 4-6).

Let us consider a metal ion such as Ti^{+3} with but one *d* electron. In the gaseous state all five *d* orbitals are of equal energy (they are degenerate), and the electron will occupy each of the orbitals with equal probability. If six negative ligands are brought close to the metal ion in an octahedral configuration along the x, y, and z axes, the *d* orbitals are no longer equivalent. An electron in either the $d_{x^2-y^2}$ or the d_{z^2} orbital will interact strongly with the negatively charged

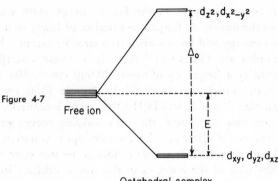

Figure 4-7

Octahedral complex

ligands compared to the small interaction if the electron is in the d_{xy}, d_{yz}, or d_{xz} orbital. The electron will prefer to occupy the orbitals in which the repulsion interaction is small. It is not obvious, but it can be demonstrated, that the repulsion energy with the $d_{x^2-y^2}$ and d_{z^2} orbitals is the same. For an octahedral distribution of six ligands around the metal ion the energy level diagram in Figure 4-7 may be constructed. Δ_o is the splitting energy caused by the octahedral field of the ligands. The single electron in Ti^{+3} would prefer to occupy the d_{xy}, d_{yz}, and d_{xz} orbitals, and thus the energy E is gained. The energy is called the crystal field stabilization energy.

Let us compare the energy of association of six ligands with two metal ions which are identical except that they contain zero and one d electron, respectively. In the former case the energy of association is simply that of electrostatic attraction (A), while in the latter the association will be the sum of A and E. Thus the complex containing the metal with one d electron would have the stronger association energy as a result of the crystal field stabilization energy.

For any particular metal ion the value of Δ_o can be experimentally determined from the absorption spectra of the complex. When light of frequency $\Delta_o/\mathbf{h}$ ($\mathbf{h}$ is Planck's constant) is passed through the complex, it will be absorbed, and a portion of the electrons in the lower energy state will be raised to the upper. At frequencies higher or lower than this the light energy will be absorbed to a smaller extent. With the complex ion $[Ti(H_2O_6]^{+3}$ there is a single absorption maximum at a frequency of about 20,000 cm^{-1} (500 mμ), which corresponds to about 57 kcal/mole (350 cm^{-1} = 1 kcal/mole). Thus Δ_o for $[Ti(H_2O)_6]^{+3}$ is 57 kcal/mole.

We may now calculate E, the extra bonding energy gained due to the one d electron. To the first approximation, the sum of the energies of the five d orbitals in the free state must equal the sum of the energies of the five d orbitals in the octahedral configuration. If we take the energy of the free state as zero, then equations 4-6 apply. Solving the latter two

$$E(d_{z^2}) \quad + \quad E(d_{x^2-y^2}) \quad + \quad E(d_{xy}) \quad + \quad E(d_{yz}) \quad + \quad E(d_{xz})$$
$$= \quad 5E(d_{free}) \quad = \quad 0$$
$$2E(d_{z^2}) \quad + \quad 3E(d_{xy}) \quad = \quad 0$$
$$E(d_{z^2}) \quad - \quad E(d_{xy}) \quad = \quad \Delta_o \qquad (4\text{-}6)$$

equations gives $E(d_{z^2}) = 0.6\Delta_o$ and $E(d_{xy}) = -0.4\Delta_o$. Thus the energy gained due to crystal field stabilization energy, E, is 0.4 × 57 = 23 kcal/mole. If all other things were the same, $[Ti(H_2O)_6]^{+3}$ should bind the waters 23 kcal/mole tighter than the neighboring d^0 ion $[Sc(H_2O)_6]^{+3}$.

It is possible for other spatial geometries to be taken if the coordination number is less than six, the two most important being the tetrahedral and planar arrangements of C.N. = 4. A diagrammatic scheme for the energy levels in these two states may be justified in the same manner as used for the octahedral system (Fig. 4-8). The tetrahedral splitting is exactly reversed from the octahedral situation, but for the same ligand Δ_t is smaller than Δ_o; $\Delta_t \approx \frac{4}{9}\Delta_o$. This suggests that in most cases the octahedral configuration will be preferred with most transition metal ions.

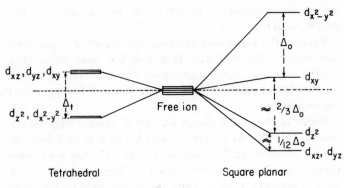

Tetrahedral   Free ion   Square planar

Figure 4-8

The planar state may be described as a distorted octahedral configuration, in which the two groups along the z axis are completely removed. The diagram given (Fig. 4-8) is for the condition of complete removal of these groups, but any intermediate position of the z axis ligands is possible, with a subsequent intermediate energy level diagram.

The d^0, d^1, d^2, d^3, d^8, d^9, and d^{10} octahedral complexes each have a single ground state, determined on the basis of the fact that the electron will take the lowest energy level possible, without unnecessary pairing of electrons. The ground states for these systems are in Figure 4-9. For all but the d^{10} configurations, some (different in each case) crystal field energy will be gained over the d^0 state. Magnetically the number of unpaired electrons per ion is the same as that expected in the valence bond theory, and in agreement with

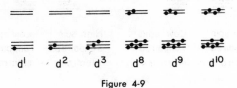

Figure 4-9

the observed magnetic moments, d^1–$1e^-$, d^2–$2e^-$, d^3–$3e^-$, d^8–$2e^-$, d^9–$1e^-$, d^{10}–$0e^-$.

Each of the remaining systems (d^4, d^5, d^6, d^7) possesses two states called the high spin and low spin states (Fig. 4-10). The high spin states have the maximum possible number of unpaired electrons, while those of low spin have the minimum.

Either of the states shown for the d^4 system may be obtained. The factors governing which one will be found are (1) the electron pairing energy, E_p, and (2) the separation energy, Δ_o. In the transition from the high to the low spin state, movement of an e^- from the upper level to the lower level will give off energy Δ_o, but energy must be expended to pair the electron with the one already present in that orbital. Thus the total energy involved will be $\Delta_o - E_p$. If Δ_o is greater than E_p, the complex will be of low spin type; if E_p is greater than Δ_o, it will be high spin. E_p is dependent on the metal ion, while Δ_o depends on the ligand. Estimates of

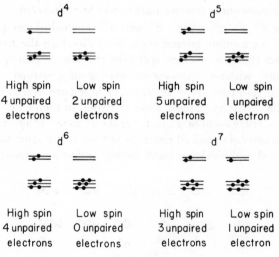

Figure 4-10

TABLE 4-2

	E_p, cm^{-1}	Δ_o, cm^{-1}	Spin
$[Mn(H_2O)_6]^{+3}$	28,000	21,000	High
$[Mn(CN)_6]^{-3}$	28,000	40,000	Low

these values made with Mn^{+3} (a d^4 ion) agree with this inter-pretation (Table 4-2).

With the analogous states for the d^5, d^6, and d^7 metal ions (Fig. 4-10) it will be noticed that in each case the high spin state corresponds to the "outer" d configuration in the va-lence bond theory, while the low spin state corresponds to the "inner" d configuration.

Similar predictions about the number of unpaired elec-trons in a complex ion may be made for the tetrahedral and planar configurations, and are in agreement with the valence bond theory and with experiment.

At this point it is well to consider the relative ability of ligands to cause splitting of the metal d orbitals. A compari-son of the changes in the absorption maxima of the com-plexes of a metal ion with several simple ligands gives a split-ting order which is the same as that found with many other metal ions. When the splitting ability is large, the absorp-tion frequencies are shifted to higher energies (lower wave-lengths). The splitting ability order for some common li-gands is $I^- < Br^- < Cl^- < F^- < OH^- < H_2O < NCS^- < NH_3 < en < dipy < NO_2^- < CN^-$. In simple terms this is the observed order of increasing electrical field shown by the ligands toward a metal ion. Although this is the usual order, reversals do occur, especially with ligands of about the same electrical field. Most of these cases are due to bonding which is not predominately electrostatic.

The "natural order" of stability for the first transition series can be explained on the basis of the crystal field theory. The order for +2 ions for many ligands is $Ca < V < Cr < Mn < Fe < Co < Ni < Cu > Zn$. The heats of hydration

$$M^{+2}_{gas} + H_2O \longrightarrow [M(H_2O)_6]^{+2}_{soln} \qquad (4-7)$$
$$\text{excess}$$

(4-7) give this order as shown by the dark circles in Figure 4-11. One might expect the ionic size of these ions to decrease regularly Ca $\longrightarrow$ Zn, and thus find that the heats of hydration increased regularly Ca $\longrightarrow$ Zn. From the graph it can be seen that the d^0, d^5, and d^{10} ions do fall on a nearly straight line, and it is significant that these are the same ions which cannot have crystal field stabilization energy. The crystal field stabilization energy for the remaining ions can be calculated from their visible spectra by a complicated method related to that used for Ti^{+3} (page 74).

When this calculated energy is subtracted from the observed hydration energies, the open circles in the graph are obtained. The "natural order" for thermodynamic stability is due to a combination of (a) a regular contraction in size leading to greater stability Ca $\longrightarrow$ Zn and (b) an irregular crystal field stabilization energy, $d^{4,9} > d^{3,8} > d^{2,7} > d^{1,6} > d^{0,5,10}$.

Since the formation of a complex in aqueous solution involves the replacement of water molecules by ligands which are usually higher on the spectrochemical scale, there will be an increase in the crystal field stabilization energy with the new ligand. This will be proportional to the crystal field stabilization energy difference between water and the ligand, in the gaseous state. Thus, the features contained in the hydration energy curve will be maintained for $-\Delta H°$ in replacement reactions (4-8, where L is above H_2O in the spectrochemical series).

$$M(H_2O)_6]^{+y} + L \longrightarrow [M(L)_6]^{+y} + 6\,H_2O \qquad (4-8)$$

The crystal field approach to bonding was developed on the basis of an electrostatic interaction between positive metal ions and the negative charge shown by anions of polar molecules. That is, the ligand electrons do not enter

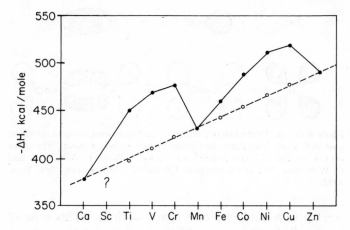

Figure 4-11. Heats of Hydration of +2 Ions. (After O. G. Holmes and D. S. McClure, *J. Chem. Phys.* **26**, 1686 (1957))

the metal orbitals and the metal *d* electrons do not enter the ligand orbitals. Refined magnetic measurements (electron spin resonance data) have since demonstrated that this ideal behavior is never completely obtained. In $[IrCl_6]^{-2}$, which contains one unpaired electron, it has been shown that the unpaired electron spends about 5% of its time in the orbitals of each chlorine atom and 70% on the metal atom. The unpaired electron is more localized with the analogous fluorine derivative, but metal-ligand orbital mixing is still observed.

π Bonding

In several classes of compounds the bonding strength and chemical properties cannot be explained solely on the basis of electrostatic attraction. The electrostatic type of bonding (commonly called σ (sigma) bonding because the bond has a center of symmetry) must be supplemented by the overlap of other orbitals. Either filled ligand orbitals may overlap with unfilled *p* or *d* metal orbitals, or filled *d* metal orbitals may

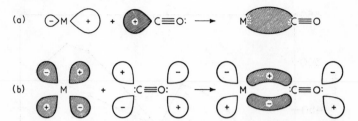

Figure 4-12. (a) Formation of the metal←carbon σ bond using an unshared pair on C atom. (b) Formation of the metal→carbon π bond. The other orbitals on the CO are omitted for clarity. (From F. A. Cotton and G. Wilkinson, "Advanced Inorganic Chemistry," Interscience, New York, 1962)

overlap with unfilled p or d ligand orbitals. This type of bond, called a π bond, has different symmetry from a σ bond (Fig. 4-12). π bonding is especially important with unsaturated ligands such as CO, NO, CN^-, py, o-phen, dipy, and certain phosphine and arsine derivatives. Usually σ and π bonds occur simultaneously and produce a stronger bond than either would alone. Two types of π bonding are commonly recognized: either a combination of σ (ligand→metal) and π (metal→ligand), or σ (ligand→metal) and π (ligand→metal). The former are generally formed with the metal in a low oxidation state (many electrons) and an unsaturated ligand (e.g., CN^-, CO), while the latter type is prevalent with saturated ligands and the metal in a high oxidation state.

The importance of π bonding can be shown in the spectrochemical series previously given (page 77). Certain groups do not occupy the positions which we would expect on the basis of their ability to "show" a negative charge to a metal ion; OH^-, for example, should have a much more negative charge than H_2O, but it gives a lower d orbital splitting, and CN^-, dipy, and NO_2^- are unusually high for weak bases. Qualitatively these facts may be understood on the basis of the two types of π bonding. The hydroxyl ion, having three unshared pairs of electrons, would have a greater tendency to back-donate electrons to the metal than water. If this should occur, the net effective charge on the metal would decrease and the splitting of the d orbitals would decrease. (The splitting energy is highly dependent on the metal ion charge: with H_2O) Mn^{+2} 7,800, Mn^{+3} 21,000 cm^{-1}. Unsaturated ligands, such as CN^-, dipy, and NO_2^-, π bond by removal of electrons from filled d orbitals and thus leave the metal ion with a higher positive charge. This tends to increase the crystal field stabilization energy compared to ligands which do not π-bond, such as NH_3 and en. The high kinetic and thermodynamic stability of carbonyls, CN^- complexes, and certain organometallic compounds is certainly due to π bonding of the latter type.

Olefin-metal ion complexes have been known for many years. Cu^+, Ag^+, Hg^{+2}, Pd^{+2}, and Pt^{+2} compounds are well established both in the solid state and in aqueous solution. In the simple compounds such as $[PtCl_3 \text{ ethylene}]^-$ the olefin is perpendicular to the plane formed by the other groups. It is believed that the bonding consists of two parts: (1) donation from the filled π orbitals of the olefin to the vacant metal orbital and (2) back-bonding from the filled metal orbitals to ligand π type orbitals.

"Sandwich" Type Compounds

The first "sandwich" compound was reported in 1951 and was called *ferrocene*, $[Fe(C_5H_5)_2]^0$. It was later shown to have a structure in which the rings are equidistant from the metal and all carbons and hydrogens are equivalent. It is extremely stable to heat, and is oxidized in aqueous solution by common oxidizing agents to $[(C_5H_5)_2Fe]^+$. Another compound of similar type is dibenzenechromium, $[(C_6H_6)_2Cr]^0$. The bonding in these complexes appears to involve an overlap between the filled π orbitals of the ligands and the empty d orbitals of the metal ion.

chapter five _____

PROPERTIES AND
REACTIONS

Stereochemistry

IN SOLUTION many inorganic complexes are slow to come to equilibrium so that it is often possible to separate and characterize geometrical and optical isomers. The situation is similar to that found with organic compounds which are slow to isomerize. However, unlike organic chemistry, the number and type of isomers are not limited by the constant coordination number of four of carbon.

We will consider the two classes of isomerism—geometrical and optical—separately, although the two types frequently are interrelated.

Geometrical Isomers. Most known geometrical isomers are found with molecules having the planar (C.N. = 4) or the octahedral (C.N. = 6) configuration. In the planar state the isomer pair illustrated in Figure 5-1 is possible with mono-

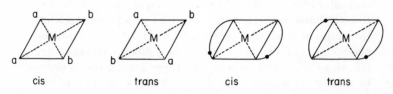

cis   trans   cis   trans

Figure 5-1   Figure 5-2

82

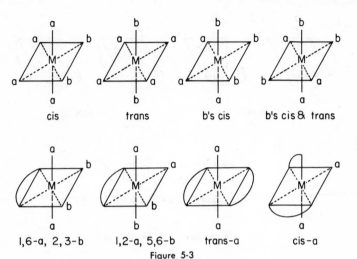

Figure 5-3

dentate ligands. With a bidentate chelating ligand, geometrical isomers are obtained only if the ligand is unsymmetrical (Fig. 5-2). The octahedral state has many possibilities. Some of the common ones appear in Figure 5-3.

Optical Isomers. These isomers exist when it is impossible to superimpose one structure upon the other even though the substances are not geometrical isomers. The common cases occur with the tetrahedral, planar, and octahedral configurations. As with the carbon compounds, four different groups surrounding a metal ion in a tetrahedral arrangement (Fig. 5-4) give rise to optical isomers, it being impossible to rotate

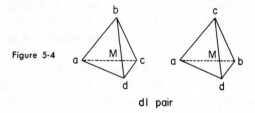

Figure 5-4

dl pair

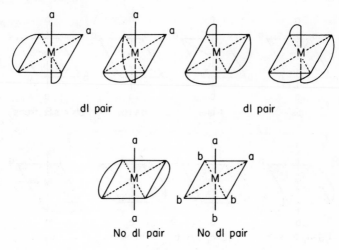

dl pair   dl pair

No dl pair   No dl pair

Figure 5-5

one structure so that the groups will occupy the same relative positions in both. With planar configurations four different groups give only geometrical isomers, but, as will be shown later, optical isomers of planar molecules are possible if unsymmetrical chelating ligands are used. Again the number of possibilities with octahedral complexes is large. A few illustrations are given in Figure 5-5.

Separation of Isomers. Because of their property differences, many geometrical isomers can be separated by simple crystallization techniques, by chromatography, or in certain cases by vacuum distillation. Optical isomers, on the other hand, can only be separated in the presence of another optically active substance. A simple method which sometimes gives a partial separation is fractional adsorption on an insoluble optically active solid such as D-quartz or D-starch. The optically active solid preferentially adsorbs one of the isomers, resulting in an enrichment of the other in the complex solution. Complete separation or resolution normally requires the formation of a salt of the *dl* complex with an optically active ion. D-Tartrate ion may be used for this purpose. The resulting salt consists of two forms, *d*-complex⁺ D-tartrate⁻ and *l*-complex⁺ D-tartrate⁻, which have different physical and chemical properties. They may be separated by fractional crystallization, and the tartrate ion replaced by an optically inactive ion. Such a separation has been carried out with $[Fe(o\text{-phen})_3]^{+2}$, giving the pure *d* and *l* forms.

The formation of a compound capable of existing in *d* and *l* forms always produces a mixture containing equal amounts of the two isomers. Since they rotate a plane of polarized light equally in opposite directions, a solution of the compounds shows no optical activity. This state of equal amounts of the *d* and *l* forms is also the equilibrium state, and therefore no change in relative amounts occurs with time. However, if the formation of the complex is carried out in the presence of a nonreacting optically active ion, unequal amounts of the *d* and *l* isomers will be formed and the complex will show some small activity. In a like manner, the addition of an optically active nonreacting ion to the *dl* form of a complex causes one of the complex forms to be thermodynamically more stable, and, if the *d* to *l* conversion is kinetically possible, a small excess of one of the complex forms will be generated.

Chemical Properties of cis-trans Isomers. A well-known ion, $[Co(en)_2CO_3]^+$, can easily be made from $CoCl_2$, ethylenediamine, and Na_2CO_3 by air oxidation. Upon treatment with aqueous HCl, the chelated CO_3^{-2} ion is replaced by water and chloride ion to form a mixture of *cis* and *trans* compounds. If this mixture of ions is slowly evaporated from HCl solution, a deep green compound crystallizes which is *trans*-$[Co(en)_2Cl_2]Cl \cdot HCl$. The *cis* isomer can be prepared by removing the HCl of crystallization by heating in air, dissolving the resulting compound in warm water, and evaporating to a small volume. The crystals deposited in the absence of excess HCl are the purple *cis*-[Co(en)$_2$Cl$_2$]Cl. *cis*-[Co(en)$_2$Cl$_2$]Cl may be nearly quantitatively converted to the *trans* form by repeated evaporation from HCl solution. These conversions have been studied in detail, and the reactions responsible for the products are known. In the initial reaction the diaquo complex is formed, which isomerizes to a mixture of *cis* and *trans* isomers. Warming with HCl causes substitution of water by chloride ion. Upon evaporation the least soluble form is removed from solution. In strong acid medium the *trans*-dichloro, as the hydrochloride, is the least soluble, while in the absence of acid the *cis*-dichloro is least soluble. The fact that nearly all of the complex is converted to either the *cis*-dichloro or the *trans*-dichloro, depending on the acidity, is due to the *cis-trans* isomerization of the aquo forms.

Aside from differences in color, geometrical isomers show differences in their reaction products. For example, the reaction of *cis*- or *trans*-[Co(en)$_2$NO$_2$Cl]$^+$ with H$_2$O quantitatively produces *cis*- or *trans*-[Co(en)$_2$NO$_2$H$_2$O]$^{+2}$, respectively. However, the analogous reaction with *cis*-[Co(en)$_2$(NH$_3$)Cl]$^{+2}$ gives both *cis* and *trans* isomers in 75:25 ratio and that with *trans*-[Co(en)$_2$(NH$_3$)Cl]$^{+2}$ gives a 20:80 *cis/trans* ratio.

Geometrical isomers also show different reaction rates. This may be illustrated by the rates of hydrolysis in acid medium of some Co^{+3} complexes (Table 5-1). It is often found that *trans* halogens are replaced by water more slowly than the isomeric *cis* forms.

Only recently have careful studies been made on the equilibria between *cis* and *trans* isomers. Some reliable values for

TABLE 5-1 [Co(X)$_5$Cl]$^{+n}$ $\rightarrow$ [Co(X$_5$)OH$_2$]$^{+(n+1)}$ + Cl$^-$ (at 25°C)

Reactant	k, min^{-1}	Reactant	k, min^{-1}
cis-[Co(en)$_2$Cl$_2$]$^+$	1.5×10^{-2}	*cis*-[Co(en)$_2$(NO$_2$)Cl]$^+$	7×10^{-3}
trans-[Co(en)$_2$Cl$_2$]$^+$	2×10^{-3}	*trans*-[Co(en)$_2$(NO$_2$)Cl]$^+$	7×10^{-4}

equilibrium constants $K = trans/cis$ in aqueous solution are listed in Table 5-2. Although few equilibrium measurements have been made on planar complexes, a series of platinum complexes have been studied and show large differences in K with different ligands (Table 5-3).

TABLE 5-2

Ion	$K, t/c$
$[Cr(H_2O)_4(NCS)_2]^+$	0.53
$[Cr(H_2O)_4(Cl_2)]^+$	0.56
$[Co(en)_2(H_2O)(NO_2)]^{+2}$	2.2

TABLE 5-3

$$cis\text{-}[Pt(MEt_3)_2Cl_2] \overset{K}{\rightleftharpoons} trans\text{-}[Pt(MEt_3)_2Cl_2]$$

M	$K, t/c$
P	12.3
As	175
Sb	1.9

cis-trans Isomerization. Earlier it was shown that *cis-trans*-$[Co(en)_2Cl_2]^+$ isomerization occurs in the presence of water, and that the isomer obtained depends on the solubilities of the complexes. All of the evidence available suggests that the mechanism of this reaction in HCl solution (where the di-aquo species does not exist in any appreciable quantity) is:

$$cis\text{-}[Co(en)_2Cl_2]^+ + H_2O \rightleftharpoons cis\text{-}[Co(en)_2(H_2O)Cl]^{+2} + Cl^-$$

$$trans\text{-}[Co(en)_2Cl_2]^+ + H_2O \rightleftharpoons trans\text{-}[Co(en)_2(H_2O)Cl]^{+2} + Cl^-$$

The isomerization occurs between the aquo-chloro species and may be visualized as occurring through dissociation to the five-coordinate intermediate of a trigonal bipyramidal structure (5-1). The five-coordinate intermediate is thought to be present in undetectably minute concentrations.

$$(5\text{-}1)$$

In methanol, where the *cis-trans* isomerization is not complicated by aquation, the violet *cis*-$[Co(en)_2Cl_2]^+$ has been observed to change to green *trans*-$[Co(en)_2Cl_2]^+$. At equilibrium the *trans* form is thermodynamically stable. Since the rate of Cl^- exchange, as radioactive Cl^{36}, is the same as the rate of loss of optical activity of *l*-$[Co(en)_2Cl_2]^+$, but considerably larger than the *cis-trans* isomerization rate, it has been suggested that a five-coordinated intermediate is also involved in this mechanism. Thus the reaction scheme is represented as in 5-2. This mechanism explains the faster rates of

Cl^- exchange and racemization since the pentacoordinated intermediate must undergo Cl^- exchange and racemization, but only a portion of the time leads to the *trans* configuration. In this case it has been estimated that 80% of the reactions of the pentacoordinated intermediate lead to the *trans* form, the other 20% giving the *cis* form.

Racemization. Just as in carbon chemistry, many coordination compounds, potentially capable of being separated into optical isomers, racemize so rapidly that separations cannot be made. Generally, ions which are labile are difficult or impossible to resolve, and, conversely, nonlabile complex ions are usually resolvable. Some ions which have been shown to exhibit optical activity are given in Table 5-4. With octahedral complexes there appear to be two main

TABLE 5-4

$[Cd(en)_3]^{+2}$	$[Cr(en)_3]^{+3}$
$[Zn(en)_3]^{+2}$	$[Co(en)_3]^{+3}$
$[Fe(o\text{-phen})_3]^{+2}$	*cis*-$[Co(en)_2(NO_2)_2]^+$
$[Pt(en)_3]^{+4}$	$[Ni(o\text{-phen})_3]^{+2}$

mechanisms by which an optically active complex may racemize (*d* or *l*-complex → *dl*-complex). These are called the intermolecular and the intramolecular processes. In some cases one process is used in preference to the other, while occasionally both processes occur simultaneously.

The *intermolecular* mechanism of racemization has been established in the cases of *d*-[Ni(*o*-phen)$_3$]$^{+2}$ and *d*-[Ni(dipy)$_3$]$^{+2}$. It is based on the fact that the rate constants for dissociation and racemization are the same over considerable ranges of temperature and acidity. This suggests that the primary step leading to these two reactions is the same, namely:

$$d\text{-[Ni(N—N)}_3]^{+2} \underset{\text{slow}}{\overset{K}{\rightleftharpoons}} dl\text{-[Ni(N—N)}_2(H_2O)_2]^{+2} + N—N \quad (5\text{-}3)$$

K is very small so that appreciable concentrations of the product are not built up. In an acid medium the reaction is pulled to the right by the subsequent reaction of the free amine with H^+_{aq} and the intermediate rapidly dissociates to Ni^{+2} and $2(N—NH^+)$. In pure water, where dissociation does not occur, the racemization has the same activation energy as it has in acidic media, suggesting that solvent conditions do not affect the mechanism. Furthermore, the kinetics of radioactive ligand (C^{14}) exchange agree with the conclusion that the primary process in water is reaction 5-3.

The racemization of *d*-[Cr(C$_2$O$_4$)$_3$]$^{-3}$ appears to be an example of an *intra*molecular reaction. Several facts support such a conclusion: (1) one cannot detect any $C_2O_4^{-2}$ in an aqueous solution of the complex; (2) the racemization takes place in the solid state; and (3) it has been demonstrated with radioactive $C_2O_4^{-2}$ that no exchange takes place between the complex and excess $C_2O_4^{-2}$ during times which give complete racemization. These experiments suggest that an oxalate ion does not come off during racemization. The possibility exists that one end of the oxalate ion may dissociate and lead to racemization. It was found that all twelve oxygens of the complex exchanged with H_2O^{18}, but the rate was considerably slower than the racemization. From this it follows that the racemization of $[Cr(C_2O_4)_3]^{-3}$ may take place *partially* by opening one of the chelate rings. The intramolecular path is visualized as going through a symmetrical trigonal prism arrangement due to distortion of all of the bonds by a twisting motion:

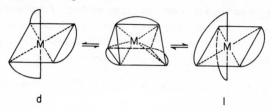

d   l

$[Fe(o\text{-}phen)_3]^{+2}$ and $[Fe(dipy)_3]^{+2}$ racemize considerably faster than they dissociate. Most probably the racemization takes place by both inter- and intramolecular mechanisms.

Some complex ions are extremely resistant to racemization. Solutions of $d\text{-}[Co(en)_3)]^{+3}$ show no loss of optical activity after three months at room temperature, and even at 100°C the reaction is extremely slow.

Oxidation State Stabilization

Many oxidation states not normal for metals can be stabilized thermodynamically, and sometimes kinetically, by coordination with a suitable ligand. An early example of this phenomenon occurred with the +2 and +3 oxidation states of cobalt. In strong $HClO_4$ media both Co^{+2} and Co^{+3} can be prepared, and it is found that the +2 state is stable but the +3 state is not. Co^{+3} rapidly and completely oxidizes Fe^{+2}, SO_3^{-2}, and even Cl^-, producing Co^{+2}. In the absence of reducing agents, Co^{+3} slowly oxidizes the solvent water, producing oxygen. In the presence of ethylenediamine, $[Co(en)_3]^{+3}$ is both kinetically and thermodynamically more stable than $[Co(en)_3]^{+2}$. The former will not oxidize most reducing agents, while the latter will reduce Fe^{+3}, O_2, H_2O_2, and many other oxidizing agents.

A qualitative explanation of the effect based on the crystal field theory will now be presented. Figure 5-6 shows the d-splitting caused by the ligands for both oxidation states.

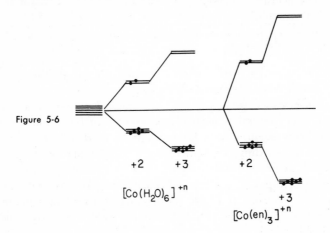

Figure 5-6

+2   +3   +2

$[Co(H_2O)_6]^{+n}$

+3

$[Co(en)_3]^{+n}$

Neglecting the electron pairing energy and the electron ionization energy, since they will be essentially constant for both ligands, the crystal field stabilization energy (CFSE) for the +2 ion is $[5(-0.4) + 2(+0.6)]\Delta_o = -0.8\Delta_o$ and for the +3 ion $[6(-0.4) + 0(+0.6)]\Delta_o = -2.4\Delta_o$. The larger negative value of the CFSE for the +3 state at any Δ_o value suggests that the +3 state is the more sensitive to the ligand field and as Δ_o increases ($H_2O \rightarrow en$) the +3 state would show a larger CFSE change than the +2 state. Therefore the +3 oxidation state of cobalt would be stabilized (compared to Co^{+2}) with ethylenediamine ligands.

Many other examples can be shown where the oxidation potential is drastically modified in the presence of a coordinating agent, and those in Table 5-5 illustrate how large this effect can be. From this it can be seen that F^- and CN^-

TABLE 5-5

	Volts[a]
$[Fe(H_2O)_x]^{+2} \rightarrow [Fe(H_2O)_x]^{+3} + e^-$	−0.77
$[FeF_6]^{-4} \rightarrow [FeF_6]^{-3} + e^-$	−0.40
$[Fe(CN)_6]^{-4} \rightarrow [Fe(CN)_6]^{-3} + e^-$	−0.36
$[Fe(dipy)_3]^{+2} \rightarrow [Fe(dipy)_3]^{+3} + e^-$	−1.10
$[Fe(o\text{-phen})_3]^{+2} \rightarrow [Fe(o\text{-phen})_3]^{+3} + e^-$	−1.14

[a] A negative potential indicates that the reduced form of the complex is a poorer reducing agent than hydrogen.

stabilize the +3 state, while dipy and o-phen stabilize the +2 state when compared with water.

Silver can exist in the +1, +2, and +3 oxidation states, but only the first is normally observed. In the presence of oxidizing agents and a ligand capable of double bonding, such as py, dipy, or o-phen, Ag^{+2} compounds are formed which are remarkably stable. The complexes $[Ag(py)_4]^{+2}$ and $[Ag(dipy)_2]^{+2}$ are colored (red to brown), have one unpaired electron, and have the ligands arranged in a plane. Similar compounds can be prepared with tripyridyl and picolinic acid.

The reduction of $[Ni(CN)_4]^{-2}$ with potassium metal dissolved in liquid NH_3 produces either a dark yellow precipitate, $K_4[Ni(CN)_4]$, or a deep red compound, $K_2Ni(CN)_3$, depending on conditions. These compounds correspond to the 0 and +1 oxidation states, respectively. Both are unstable in the presence of air, but $[Ni(CN)_3]^{-2}$ is somewhat stable in water solution. It may also be produced in alkaline solution by the reduction of $K_2[Ni(CN)_4]$ with Sn.

Rules governing the effect of a ligand on the relative stabilities of the oxidation states of a metal are complicated by the problem of separating kinetic and equilibrium stabilities. The factors which govern the amounts of each oxidation state at equilibrium are not the same as those which affect the kinetic parameters. Thermodynamically it appears that: (a) low oxidation states will be favored with ligands having reducing power or with reducing solvents; (b) basic conditions will favor high oxidation states and acid conditions low; and (c) the electronic configurations of the oxidation states coupled with the ligand field strength may stabilize either the upper or lower state.

Kinetic stabilization of a particular oxidation state may be effected through (a) complex insolubility and (b) the use of bulky ligands which prevent otherwise favorable reaction routes through steric hindrance.

Acid-Base Properties

The acidity of metal ion salts can be accounted for on the basis of hydrolysis of the coordinated water molecules:

$$[M(H_2O)_x]^{+n} \overset{K_a}{\rightleftharpoons} [M(H_2O)_{x-1}(OH)]^{+(n-1)} + H^+_{aq}$$

Provided only a small fraction of the metal is hydrolyzed, this equilibrium is not complicated by further reactions. Some values of pK_a for common ions are listed in Table 5-6.

When more extensive hydrolysis occurs, it usually is accompanied by polymerization. The exact nature of these polymers is not known in most instances. The general forms seem to be:

$$[M(H_2O)_5OH]^{+(n-1)} + [M(H_2O)_6]^{+n} \rightleftharpoons$$

$$[(H_2O)_5M\overset{H}{-}O-M(OH_2)_5]^{+(2n-1)} + H_2O$$

$$2[M(H_2O)_5OH]^{+(n-1)} \rightleftharpoons [(H_2O)_4M\begin{matrix} \overset{H}{O} \\ \diagup \diagdown \\ \underset{H}{O} \end{matrix}M(OH_2)_4]^{+(2n-2)} + 2H_2O$$

The polymerization process does not usually stop at the dimer stage, and so the interpretation of hydrolysis studies is extremely difficult, since many different equilibria will explain the same experimental data. An addition problem is

TABLE 5-6. Acid Dissociation Constants of Aquated Metal Ions (pK_a)

$[Al(H_2O)_6]^{+3}$	4.9	$[Sc(H_2O)_x]^{+3}$	5.1
$[Fe(H_2O)_6]^{+3}$	3.0	$[Cd(H_2O)_x]^{+2}$	10
$[Cr(H_2O)_6]^{+3}$	3.9	$[Pb(H_2O)_x]^{+2}$	7.8

often present, that of aging. The hydrolysis products apparently do not reach equilibrium rapidly because of slow formation of oxo bridges (M—O—M). This may lead to precipitation.

The initial stages of Fe^{+3} hydrolysis have been studied in some detail using pH, spectral, and magnetic measurements. The following scheme explains the experimental results:

$$[Fe(H_2O)_6]^{+3} \overset{K_1}{\rightleftharpoons} [Fe(H_2O)_5OH]^{+2} + H^+$$
$$K_1 = 9 \times 10^{-4}$$

$$[Fe(H_2O)_6]^{+3} \overset{K_2}{\rightleftharpoons} [Fe(H_2O)_4(OH)_2]^+ + 2H^+$$
$$K_2 = 5 \times 10^{-7}$$

$$2[Fe(H_2O)_6]^{+3} \overset{K_3}{\rightleftharpoons} [(Fe(H_2O)_4(OH))_2]^{+4} + 2H^+$$
$$K_3 = 1 \times 10^{-3}$$

$[Fe(H_2O)_6]^{+3}$, $[Fe(H_2O)_5OH]^{+2}$, and $[Fe(H_2O)_4(OH)_2]^+$ are paramagnetic, while the dimer $[(Fe(H_2O)_4(OH))_2]^{+4}$ is diamagnetic. The dimer has the structure given in Figure 5-7,

Figure 5-7

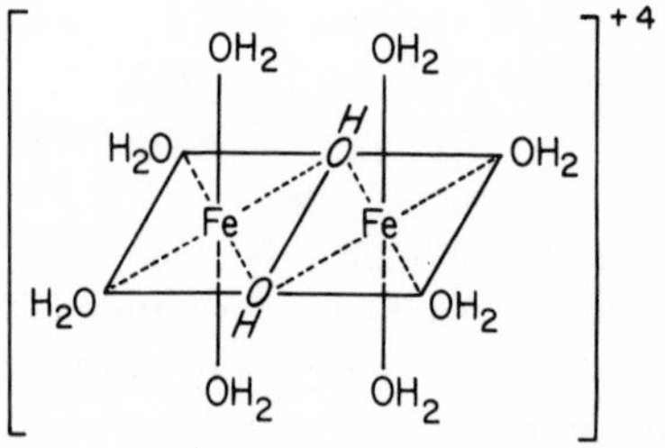

and its low magnetic moment is due to pairing of electron spins between the two iron ions. Other dimers of similar structure are also diamagnetic, e.g., $[Cl_5Ru-O-RuCl_5]^{-4}$.

The presence of amino groups in the coordination sphere, in addition to water molecules, puts the interpretation of pH titration studies on a more firm basis. This follows because the coordinated amine hydrogens are considerably less acidic than water, and thus a number of complications do not arise. Some representative examples are given in Table 5-7. It is apparent from this that with +3 ions the acidity increases with the number of water molecules.

TABLE 5-7 $\quad R_5M-OH_2 \overset{K_a}{\rightleftharpoons} R_5M-OH + H^+$

Complex	pK_a	Complex	pK_a
$[Co(NH_3)_4(NO_2)H_2O]^{+2}$	6	$[Co(NH_3)_4(H_2O)_2]^{+3}$	5.2
$[Co(NH_3)_5H_2O]^{+3}$	5.7	$[Co(NH_3)_3(H_2O)_3]^{+3}$	4.7

The ammine group may also lose a hydrogen ion by ionization. Under the usual conditions this only becomes apparent with the third transition metals. For

$$[Pt(NH_3)_6]^{+4} \rightarrow [Pt(NH_3)_5(NH_2)]^{+3} + H^+ \quad (5-14)$$

$pK_a = 7.9$. In some cases the dissociation becomes so complete that only the amino-amido complex can be isolated such as in $[Os^V(en)(en - H)_2]^{+3}$ and $[Re^V(CH_3NH_2)_4-(CH_3NH)_2]^{+3}$.

The major factors governing the acidity of a complex ion are:

(a) The acidic properties of the free ligand. Coordination of a ligand usually makes the ligand more acidic because of a net drain of electrons to the metal $M-O-H^{\delta+}$. However, the metal effect is about the same for different ligands, and thus the more acidic a free ligand is the more acidic it will be in a complex. For instance, H_2O is more acidic than NH_3, and thus $[Co(H_2O)_6]^{+3}$ is more acidic than $[Co(NH_3)_6]^{+3}$.

(b) The higher the complex charge, the higher the acidity. This results from the greater repulsion of a proton by the more positive cation.

(c) Oxidation state. The higher the oxidation state for commonly charged ions, the greater the acidity. This is shown by the fact that $[Pt(NH_3)_5Cl]^{+3}$ is more acidic than $[Co(NH_3)_6]^{+3}$.

(d) Strength of ligand bond. It is generally accepted that the second and third transition metals bind ligands more tightly than the first series. A logical consequence of this is the greater acidity of the second and third transition complexes. In line with this is the fact that $[Pt(NH_3)_4]^{+2} > [Pd(NH_3)_4]^{+2} > [Ni(NH_3)_4]^{+2}$ in acidity.

(e) Statistical effect. The larger the number of acidic ligands, the greater the probability that one of them will dissociate. Thus diaquo ammines are usually more acidic than monoaquo ammines, other factors being equal.

(f) Size. It is generally found that the smaller the ion, the more acidic its complexes. This, too, may be rationalized on the basis of the repulsion of the proton because of the close proximity of the ligand to the charged metal ion.

No doubt many other effects are operative in the acidity of complex ions. This is demonstrated by the geometrical effect seen with *cis-trans* isomers:

	K_1	K_2
cis-$[Pt(NH_3)_2(H_2O)_2]^{+2}$	2.8×10^{-6}	4.8×10^{-8}
trans-$[Pt(NH_3)_2(H_2O)_2]^{+2}$	4.8×10^{-5}	4.2×10^{-8}

This leaves no doubt that in planar molecules at least, the group opposite the water molecule has an effect on its acidity.

Ligand Exchange

Octahedral Substitution. Much of our knowledge of octahedral substitution mechanisms comes from the well-studied Co^{+3} and Cr^{+3} ions. The slowness of their reactions, coupled with the ease of preparation of the compounds, has facilitated their study.

Let us consider a simple substitution (eq. 5-5) and two paths which may be taken during this reaction.

$$[(Co(NH_3)_5Cl]^{+2} + H_2O \rightarrow [Co(NH_3)_5(H_2O)]^{+3} + Cl^- \quad (5-5)$$

The *dissociation* of a chloride ion would produce a penta-coordinated intermediate of very limited stability. It probably has square pyramidal geometry and in the presence of a large excess of solvent water molecules would rapidly introduce water to again complete the coordination sphere (5-6). This type of substitution is often called a dissociative process.

Short–lived
intermediate

Another likely path is *displacement*. The incoming water group may attach itself to the metal ion and thereby increase it to a coordination number of 7. The most likely geometry for this is the pentagonal bipyramid. Either at the same time as water introduction, or shortly thereafter, the chloride ion would leave, completing the substitution (5-7). Both the dissociation from, and the addition of a group to, the complex would require considerable energy (about 100 kcal/mole), and, since the activation energy for this type of

Short—lived
intermediate

$$[Co(NH_3)_5Cl]^{+2} + H_2O \xrightarrow{slow} \cdots \xrightarrow[-Cl^-]{rapid} \cdots \quad (5-7)$$

reaction is of the order of 20–30 kcal/mole, neither pure mechanism can be seriously considered. The majority of the evidence of cobalt(III) and chromium(III) substitution reactions favors a modified dissociative type mechanism. In descriptive terms, the chloride ion moves out, slightly assisted by attraction to the solvent, and at some critical distance a water molecule moves into the coordination shpere, expelling the chloride ion.

In basic media the same reactions are often 10^5 times faster, and the kinetics are second order: rate = k[complex][OH$^-$] for the reaction

$$[Co(NH_3)_5Cl]^{+2} + OH^- \rightarrow [Co(NH_3)_5OH]^{+2} + Cl^-$$

Although this suggests that the OH$^-$ attacks the complex in an associative mechanism, there is convincing evidence that again dissociation plays the dominant role. In this reaction scheme (5-8) the OH$^-$ removes a proton from an amino group, assisting in the dissociation of the chloride ion. This is followed by rapid addition of solvent water to give the product.

$$[Co(NH_3)_5Cl]^{+2} + OH^- \xrightarrow{rapid} [Co(NH_3)_4(NH_2)Cl]^+ + H_2O$$

$$[Co(NH_3)_4(NH_2)Cl]^+ \xrightarrow{slow} [Co(NH_3)_4(NH_2)]^{+2} + Cl^-$$

$$[Co(NH_3)_4(NH_2)]^{+2} + H_2O \xrightarrow{rapid} [Co(NH_3)_5OH]^{+2} \quad (5-8)$$

Two main lines of evidence substantiate this mechanism:

(a) with complexes containing nitrogen-bound ligands having no nitrogen hydrogens, the rate is essentially independent of OH⁻, and (b) the existence of the five-coordinated intermediate has been shown. This general type of mechanism is called "substitution, nucleophilic, first-order conjugated base," S_N1CB.

Planar Substitution. Considering the vacant spaces at the top and bottom of a planar complex, one might expect that an S_N2 mechanism would be more likely with a planar than with an octahedral complex. In a modified way this prediction turns out to be true. However, it has been shown conclusively that the "vacant positions" are actually occupied by solvent molecules or ions, although they are held loosely and are quite labile. Thus the groups above and below the plane may easily be replaced by other reagents in solution.

Most replacement reactions of planar complexes follow the rate law: rate = k_1[complex] + k_2[complex][reactant], which suggests simultaneous operation of two paths: a dissociative (5-9) and a displacement (5-10) path. A reaction of this type is

$$[Pt(NH_3)_3Cl]^+ \;+\; R \;\rightarrow\; [Pt(NH_3)_3R]^{+2} \;+\; Cl^-$$

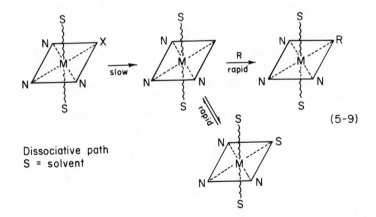

(5-9)

Dissociative path
S = solvent

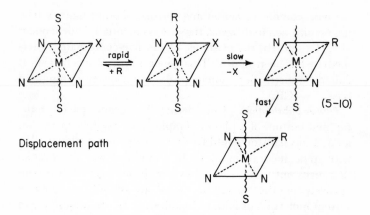

Displacement path

(5-10)

The first term in the rate law is determined by the dissociative path since the generation of the reactive intermediate does not involve the reactant R. The displacement path provides the second term in the rate law since the generation of the activated state involves the reactant group R.

The values of k_1 and k_2 depend on the metal ion, the nonreacting ligands, the reactant ligand and the solvent. For most Pt^{+2} complexes the order of reactant activity is $SCN^- > I^- > N_3^- > NO_2^- > NH_3 > Cl^- > OH^-$. The extremely low value for OH^- is of interest since it shows exactly opposite behavior with Co^{+3} and Cr^{+3}.

Isotopic Exchange. The use of labeled ligands has helped considerably in the understanding of reaction mechanisms, and occasionally in determining the structure of short-lived complexes.

The exchange of deuterium between water and coordinated amines:

$$[Co(ND_3)_6]^{+3} + H_2O \rightleftharpoons [Co(NH_3)_6]^{+3} + HDO$$

has received some study. It was found to be generally true that the rate law was: rate = k[complex][OH^-]. This was interpreted in terms of mechanism 5-11. The amide form is

$$[Co(ND_3)_6]^{+3} + OH^- \rightleftharpoons [Co(ND_3)_5(ND_2)]^{+2} + HDO$$

$$[Co(ND_3)_5(ND_2)]^{+2} + H^+ \rightleftharpoons [Co(ND_3)_5(ND_2H)]^{+3} \quad (5\text{-}11)$$

present in extremely small amounts, making the last step slow. The rates of deuterium exchange for various complexes correlate well with their acidity.

The $Cl^{*-}-AuCl_4^-$ exchange has produced evidence for the transitory existence of the unstable $+2$ state of gold. With ordinary distilled water, rapid induced exchange was observed for the first portion of the reaction, after which exchange proceeded at a slower rate. A detailed study showed that traces of certain reducing agents, notably, Fe^{+2}, were responsible for the induced exchange. Although one-electron reducing agents (Fe^{+2}, VO^{+2}) were capable of inducing exchange, two-electron reducing agents (Sn^{+2}, Sb^{+3}) were ineffective, although they reduced $AuCl_4^-$ to $AuCl_2^-$. Furthermore, $AuCl_2^-$ did not exert a catalytic effect. Thus it was suggested that some form of Au^{+2} was formed by one electron reduction which instantaneously exchanged with the Cl^- of the solution. From a kinetic study, mechanism 5-12 was suggested. The catalytic effect would continue until exchange was complete, unless a chain terminating reaction took place. This probably was the disproportionation of Au^{+2} to Au^+ and Au^{+3}.

$$Fe^{+2} + [Au\overset{*}{C}l_4]^- \rightarrow Fe^{+3} + [Au^{+2}\overset{*}{C}l_x]$$

$$[Au^{+2}\overset{*}{C}l_x] + Cl^- \xrightarrow[\text{rapid}]{\text{very}} [Au^{+2}Cl_x] + \overset{*}{C}l^-$$

$$[Au^{+2}Cl_x] + Au\overset{*}{C}l_4^- \rightarrow [Au^{+2}\overset{*}{C}l_x] + [AuCl_4]^- \quad (5\text{-}12)$$

In this connection, a known compound of the formula $KAuCl_3$ would conceivably contain gold in the $+2$ oxidation state. However, the addition of $KAuCl_3$ to $[AuCl_4]^-$ solutions exchanging with $\overset{*}{C}l^-$ did not cause catalysis, suggesting that it does not contain +2 gold. It has been shown that $KAuCl_3$ is a 1:1 combination of $KAuCl_2$ and $KAuCl_4$.

The number of water molecules attached in the first coordination sphere of Cr^{+3} has been shown to be 6 by the use of H_2O^{18}. This is one of the few ions whose coordination number with water in aqueous solution is known. A quantitative description of the technique is too lengthy for this presentation, but in essence it consisted of dissolving a salt of $[Cr(H_2O)_6]^{+3}$ in water containing H_2O^{18} and quickly precipitating the hexaquochromium salt. Analysis of the water from the salt by mass spectrometry showed the absence of H_2O^{18}. If the salt had converted to a coordination number lower or higher than six, some of the O^{18}-enriched solvent water would have been found in the coordinated water. Thus it was established that the formula in water solution is $[Cr(H_2O)_6]^{+3}$, and kinetic measurements showed a half-time of exchange to be about 40 hours.

A bridged path operates in most Cr^{+2}–Cr^{+3} exchanges. With the aquated ions the rate of chromium exchange is extremely slow ($k = 10^{-5}$ min^{-1}), but the presence of a negative ion in the Cr^{+3} coordination sphere increases the rate drastically (Table 5-8). The electron exchange occurs through a bridged intermediate (eqs. 5-13). Thus electron

$$[\overset{*}{C}r(H_2O)_6]^{+2} + [Cr(H_2O)_5Cl]^{+2} \rightleftharpoons$$

$$[(H_2O)_5\overset{*}{C}r^{II}—Cl—Cr^{III}(H_2O)_5]^{+4} + H_2O$$

$$[(H_2O)_5\overset{*}{C}r^{II}—Cl—Cr^{III}(H_2O)_5]^{+4} \rightarrow$$

$$[(H_2O)_5\overset{*}{C}r^{III}—Cl—Cr^{II}(H_2O)_5]^{+4} \rightarrow$$

$$[\overset{*}{C}r(H_2O)_5Cl]^{+2} + [Cr(H_2O)_6]^{+2} \quad (5\text{-}13)$$

TABLE 5-8

Ion	Relative rate	Ion	Relative rate
$[Cr(H_2O)_6]^{+3}$	1	$[Cr(H_2O)_5Br]^{+2}$	10^7
$[Cr(H_2O)_5Cl]^{+2}$	10^5	$[Cr(H_2O)_5OH]^{+2}$	10^6

exchange causes the chloride ion to move from one chromium atom to the other without loss to the solvent.

The rate of ammonia exchange using NH_3-N^{15} (5-14) is

$$[MX_6]^{+n} + \overset{*}{X} \rightleftharpoons [MX_5\overset{*}{X}]^{+n} + X \quad (X = amine) \quad (5\text{-}14)$$

quite dependent on the metal ion (Table 5-9). It is also dependent on the number of coordinating positions of the ligand, since k for NH_3 > en > diethylenetriamine.

TABLE 5-9. Rates of Isotopic NH_3 Exchange

	$t_{1/2}$	Temperature, °C
$[Cr(NH_3)_6]^{+3}$	25 hr	25
$[Co(NH_3)_6]^{+3}$	11 hr	25
$[Ag(NH_3)_2]^+$, $[Ni(NH_3)_6]^{+2}$, $[Cu(NH_3)_4]^{+2}$	Complete in 10 min or less	−34

Reactions of Coordinated Ligands

The reactivities of coordinated ligands have not been carefully explored until recent years, but there were some early experiments indicating the importance and usefulness of this type of reaction. Werner suggested that since the hexammine is formed upon the oxidation of $[Co(NH_3)_5NCS]^{+2}$, the thiocyanate group must be attached through its nitrogen:

$$[(NH_3)_5Co(NCS)]^{+2} \xrightarrow{\text{oxidation}}$$
$$[(NH_3)_5Co(NH_3)]^{+3} + CO_2 + SO_2$$

In a like manner a nitro group was reduced to a coordinated amine, suggesting that the nitro group was attached through its nitrogen:

$$[Pt(en)(NH_3)NO_2]^+ \xrightarrow[H^+]{Zn} [Pt(en)(NH_3)_2]^{+2}$$

Generally, ligands have considerably lower reactivities when coordinated than in their free state. In certain cases the free ligand is so unstable that it can only be formed as a complex with a metal ion (5-15). A few examples will show

$$(5\text{-}15)$$

the variety of reactions which may be accomplished. In some cases the same complex can be made either by preforming the ligand or by reaction with a complex (5-16). Sometimes ligand displacement from the coordination sphere occurs

$$(5\text{-}16)$$

$$[\text{Ni(dmg)}_2]^0 + \text{CH}_3\text{C}-\text{Cl} \;\longrightarrow\; [\text{Ni(H dmg)Cl}_2]^0 + \left(-\overset{\text{CH}_3}{\underset{}{\text{C}}}=\text{N}-\text{O}-\text{C}-\text{CH}_3\right)_2 \tag{5-17}$$

$$\left[\text{Co}\,(\overset{\text{CH}}{\underset{\text{O}\cdots\text{O}}{\overset{|}{\text{C}=\text{C}}}})^{R}_{R}\right]^0_3 + \text{Br}_2 \;\longrightarrow\; \left[\text{Co}\,(\overset{\text{C}-\text{Br}}{\underset{\text{O}\cdots\text{O}}{\overset{|}{\text{C}=\text{C}}}})^{R}_{R}\right]^0_3 + \text{HBr} \tag{5-18}$$

$$\left[\text{Cu}\,(\overset{\text{O}=\text{C}}{\underset{\text{N}-\text{C}-(\text{CH}_2)_2\text{NH}_2}{\text{H}_2}})\right]^0_2 \xrightarrow{\;\text{CH}_3\text{C}-\text{Cl}\;} \left[\text{Cu}\,(\overset{\text{O}=\text{C}}{\underset{\text{N}-\text{C}-(\text{CH}_2)_2-\text{N}-\text{C}-\text{CH}_3}{\overset{}{\text{H}_2}}})\right]^0_2 \tag{5-19}$$

$$\left[(\text{NH}_3)_5\text{Co}-\text{O}-\text{C}\;\;\text{C}-\text{CH}\right]^{+2} \xrightarrow{\;\text{H}_2\text{O}_2\;} \left[(\text{NH}_3)_5\text{Co}-\text{O}-\text{C}\;\;\text{C}-\text{OH}\right]^{+2}$$

$$\xrightarrow[\text{H}^+]{\text{MnO}_4^-} \text{Co}^{+2} + \text{HOOC}-\text{COOH} + \text{NH}_4^+ \tag{5-20}$$

(5-17). Occasionally the ligand modification does not result in metal-ligand bond rupture (5-18). The reaction of a terminal group is often only slightly affected by the metal ion (5-19). Often metal ion coordination protects the coordinated groups from reaction, and provides a method for selective action. In other cases, however, "end reaction" results in reaction at the coordinated site as well (5-20). In reaction 5-20 a one-electron oxidation takes place at the end of the chain followed by an electron transfer from the ligand to the Co^{+3}. In essence, MnO_4^- removes one electron and Co^{+3} the other in the oxidation of the aldehyde.

Numerous investigations have involved the catalytic properties of complexes. One of the most interesting is the catalytic behavior of solutions of Co^{+2} and CN^- in the presence of molecular hydrogen. These solutions have the ability to hydrogenate various organic olefins at rapid rates. The exact mechanism is not known, but most of the features correspond to the mechanism 5-21. It is noteworthy that only

$$Co^{+2} \ + \ 5\,CN^- \ \rightarrow \ [Co(CN)_5]^{-3}$$

$$2\,[Co(CN)_5]^{-3} \ + \ H:H \ \rightarrow \ 2\,[Co(CN)_5(\cdot H)]^{-3}$$

$$[Co(CN)_5(\cdot H)]^{-3} \ + \ H_2C{=}CH{-}CH{=}CH_2 \ \rightarrow$$

$$[Co(CN)_5C_4H_7]^{-3}$$

$$[Co(CN)_5C_4H_7]^{-3} \ + \ [Co(CN)_5(\cdot H)]^{-3} \ \rightarrow$$

$$2\,[Co(CN)_5]^{-3} \ + \ C_4H_8 \quad (5\text{-}21)$$

one of the double bonds is reduced. Also the butenes produced are primarily *trans*-2-butene and 1-butene with only traces of *cis*-2-butene. The ratio of the products is dependent on the Co/CN ratio. This reaction illustrates how effective certain coordination compounds are at room temperature in reactions of even such an inert substance as molecular hydrogen.

Mechanisms of Reaction

Many interesting experiments may be conducted utilizing isotopic atoms, which give us a remarkable insight into the intermediate steps in a reaction. Such an instance is the reaction of SO_3^{-2} with ClO_3^- to produce SO_4^{-2} and Cl^-. If the reaction is carried out in water enriched in O^{18}, the resulting SO_4^{-2} contains practically none of the O^{18} from the solvent. We infer, then, that since an oxygen is added to the SO_3^{-2}, and it did not come from the solvent, it must have been obtained from ClO_3^-. This was demonstrated by labeling the ClO_3^- with O^{18}. The SO_4^{-2} which was produced contained one O^{18}. These experiments strongly suggest a bridged activated state followed by electron transfer in which an atom moves quantitatively from one ion to the other, as shown in the following series of reactions.

Further reduction

In certain instances it is possible to determine the structure of a substance by a careful application of isotopic methods. The addition of $[Ni(H_2O)_x]^{+2}$ to $K_2[Ni(CN)_4]$ solutions produces a precipitate whose formula is $Ni(CN)_2$. However, if radioactive $^{63}Ni^{+2}$ is added to $K_2[Ni(CN)_4]$ in a neutral medium, and the resulting precipitate quickly treated with alkaline dimethylglyoxime, the $[Ni(dmg)_2]^0$ produced contains all of the nickel activity. Thus, in the $Ni(CN)_2$ precipitate, there are two kinds of nickel which do not mix. This is explained on the basis of 5-22, which leads to the conclusion that the precipitate has to be $Ni[Ni(CN)_4]$.

$$\overset{*}{Ni}{}^{+2} \quad + \quad [Ni(CN)_4]^{-2} \quad \rightarrow \quad \overset{*}{Ni}[Ni(CN)_4] \downarrow$$

$$\overset{*}{Ni}[Ni(CN)_4] \quad + \quad 2\,dmgH \quad \rightarrow$$

$$[\overset{*}{Ni}(dmg)_2]^0 \quad + \quad [Ni(CN)_4]^{-2} \quad + \quad 2\,H^+ \quad (5\text{-}22)$$

The reaction of $[(NH_3)_5CoOH_2]^{+3}$ with NO_2^-–HNO_2 has been of interest to investigators for some time. It is a two-step reaction involving the formation of the nitrito complex which slowly rearranges to the nitro complex. The reacting species are thought to be N_2O_3, formed by dimerization of and loss of water from $2HNO_2$, and the hydroxo form of the complex. When the aquo complex is labeled with O^{18}, it is found that the nitrito complex contains all of the heavier oxygen isotope, indicating that the Co—O bond is not broken

$$[(NH_3)_5Co\text{—}\overset{*}{O}H]^{+2} \quad + \quad N_2O_3 \quad \rightarrow$$

$$[(NH_3)_5Co\text{—}\overset{*}{O}NO]^{+2} \quad + \quad HNO_2 \quad (5\text{-}23)$$

(5-23). The nitrito-nitro rearrangement occurs intramolecularly, as shown by carrying out the reaction in O^{18}-enriched water and NO_2^-. Since the nitro complex was shown not to be enriched in O^{18}, the nitro group must have remained attached to the metal ion during rearrangement. This process is viewed as occurring by equation 5-24.

$$[(NH_3)_5Co-ONO]^{+2} \rightarrow \left[(NH_3)_5Co \overset{O}{\underset{N-O}{\diagdown}} \right]^{+2} \rightarrow$$

$$[(NH_3)_5Co-NO_2]^{+2} \quad (5\text{-}24)$$

Electron exchange coupled with atom transfer has been used to explain the products of a number of oxidation-reduction reactions involving Cr^{+2}–Co^{+3} complexes:

$$[Cr(H_2O)_6]^{+2} + [(NH_3)_5CoCl]^{+2} \xrightarrow{H^+}$$

$$[Cr(H_2O)_5Cl]^{+2} + Co^{+2} + 5\,NH_4^+$$

The surprising fact about this reaction is the production of green-colored $[Cr(H_2O)_5Cl]^{+2}$, since $[Cr(H_2O)_6]^{+3}$ reacts very slowly with Cl^-. Experiments utilizing radioactive $^{36}Cl^-$ have shown that all of the $[Cr(H_2O)_5Cl]^{+2}$ chlorine comes from the cobalt complex, even if excess HCl is present during the reaction. More extensive work has shown that the activated state is $[(H_2O)_5Cr^{II}-Cl-Co^{III}(NH_3)_5]^{+4}$, which transfers an electron from Cr^{+2} to Co^{+3}, producing nonlabile Cr^{+3} and labile Co^{+2}. The dimer then breaks into the products. This general mechanism applies to the transfer of a large number of negative ions, and may be applicable to different metal ion systems.

chapter six

APPLICATIONS

THE APPLICATIONS of coordination chemistry are so numerous that only brief mention of some of the more common ones can be made. In most instances they are employed primarily in the laboratory, but some are found in industry.

The use of complexes as precipitating agents for analysis or separations has long been of importance. The ferrocyanide ion, for example, forms sparingly soluble salts with many metal ions including Zn^{+2}, Ag^{+2}, and Cu^{+2}. Other examples include the separation of Ni^{+2} from Co^{+2} by precipitation of the former with dmg and the separation of K^+ from Na^+ by precipitation of potassium ion with $[Co(NO_2)_6]^{-3}$. Hexachloroplatinum(IV) and $[AuCl_4]^-$ are convenient precipitants for organic amine salts and are often used in their characterization.

In aqueous medium few metals can be successfully deposited in a smooth coherent plate from their simple aquo complexes. In most instances they must be coordinated to some group which provides a suitable environment for a smoothly adhering deposit. Satisfactory complexes often result with CN^-, OH^-, or certain amines, and such ions as $[Au(CN)_4]^-$, $[Ag(CN)_2]^-$, $[Sn(OH)_6]^{-4}$, and $[Cd(CN)_6]^{-4}$ are extensively used for this purpose. Frequently other ligands are also added to the electroplating bath to improve its efficiency and throwing power and the surface characteristics of the plate. In general, however, the specific nature of their interaction is not known, and the process of plating is still in the state of trial and error, and is often classified as an "art."

Preparation of New Compounds

In recent years it has become apparent that a knowledge of reaction mechanisms can be helpful in predicting the success of a particular mode of synthesis. In certain cases it may even suggest methods of synthesis. Along these lines we will describe two areas in which new, previously unpreparable compounds were isolated through this knowledge.

Several nitrito-cobalt(III) complexes ($R_5Co-ONO$) have been known for many years, but it is only recently that the mechanism of formation and rearrangement has been understood. These complexes are metastable isomers of the stable nitro (R_5Co-NO_2) complexes. The reaction mechanism was described in Chapter 5. Kinetic studies suggested N_2O_3 as the reactant, and also provided the important conclusion that the $Co-O$ bond is not broken.

Recently several new nitrito compounds have been made based on this mechanism, and more particularly on the fact that it is successful when the metal to oxygen bond is substitution inert. Thus it is not necessary to break high energy metal-oxygen bonds to form the nitrito complexes. Using essentially the same procedure as with the Co^{+3} complexes, $[Pt(NH_3)_5ONO]^{+3}$, $[Ir(NH_3)_5ONO]^{+2}$, and $[Rh(NH_3)_5-ONO]^{+3}$ were prepared in a state of high purity. These complexes had not been observed previously, even though a normal route to the preparation of $[M(NH_3)_5NO_2]^{+n}$ species is by the reaction of the aquo complex with acidic NO_2^-. They were not observed because the reaction mixtures were heated for long periods, following the belief that most reactions of Pt^{+4}, Ir^{+3}, and Rh^{+4} are slow. This heating caused the nitrito compound to rearrange to the nitro isomer. When it was recognized that metal-oxygen replacement did not need to take place, a rapid rate of formation of the nitrito complex was expected, and subsequent low temperature reactions produced the new compounds.

Although a large number of coordination compounds of

Pt^{+4} are known, many of the type *trans*-$[Pt(en)_2X_2]^{+2}$, the preparation of *trans*-$[Pt(en)_2(SCN)_2]^{+2}$ had not been successful up to 1959. At that time a preparation was accomplished using a knowledge of the mechanism by which many ligand exchanges occur in Pt^{+4} reactions.

Studies on Cl^- exchange and changes in optical activity had shown that ligand exchange of *trans*-$[Pt(en)_2X_2]^{+2}$ type species is catalyzed by the presence of the Pt^{+2} complex (in this case $[Pt(en)_2]^{+2}$). These studies suggested that the substitution reaction (6-1) occurs via a bridged intermediate

$$[Pt(en)_2Cl_2]^{+2} + 2\overset{*}{C}l^- \xrightarrow{\text{catalyst}} [Pt(en)_2\overset{*}{C}l_2]^{+2} + 2Cl^- \quad (6\text{-}1)$$

$(Pt^{+4}\text{—}Cl\text{—}Pt^{+2})$. It appeared that this catalytic path would also be operative with the SCN^- ion and would provide a low activation energy path by which the new compound, *trans*-$[Pt(en)_2(SCN)_2]^{+2}$, could be prepared. Experimentally it was found that in the presence of the catalyst, $[Pt(en)_2]^{+2}$, the reaction proceeded to completion within a few seconds, while the uncatalyzed reaction was considerably slower and was accompanied by side reactions. Thus a knowledge of reaction mechanisms helped formulate the correct experimental conditions for the preparation of pure *trans*-$[Pt(en)_2(SCN)_2]^{+2}$.

Analysis and Metal Separation

An interesting example of the design of ligands to fulfill a particular application involves the synthesis of an α-amine-oxime, which allows the analytical determination of nickel(II) in the presence of copper(II). The complexes of Ni^{+2} and Cu^{+2} with an α-aminoxime have the structure given in Figure 6-1, and with the former metal are diamagnetic and planar. It was observed that with the PnAO complexes, EDTA reacted very slowly with the Ni^{+2} but rapidly with the Cu^{+2} complex to produce the metal-EDTA complexes.

The analytical procedure consists of adding an excess of

Figure 6-1

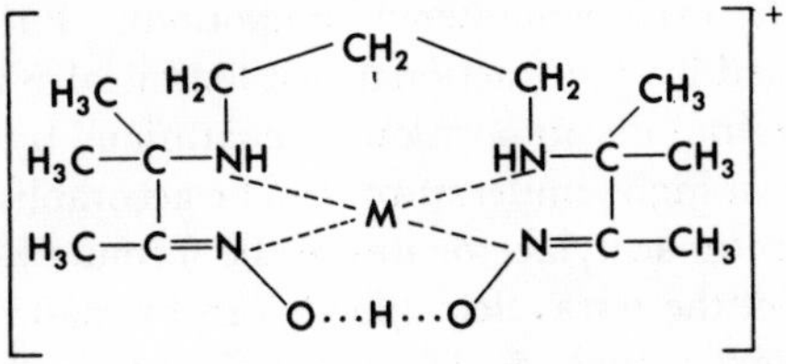

PnAO to one of two samples containing an unknown amount of Ni^{+2} and Cu^{+2} in basic medium, whereupon the α-amineoxime complexes are formed. Then a large excess of EDTA is added to both samples, and the absorbance difference between the two samples measured at the absorbance maximum of the Ni^{+2}-α-amineoxime complex. This absorbance is directly related to the concentration of Ni^{+2} in the original unknown solution. The spectra of the Ni-α-amineoxime complex and the copper-EDTA complex are widely different, and no absorption at the nickel complex peak is exhibited by the copper-EDTA complex.

The absorption spectra of the copper- and nickel-α-amineoxime complexes overlap and the two of EDTA overlap at most frequencies, but copper-EDTA and nickel-α-amineoxime do not. The success of this method depends on the fact that the copper-α-amineoxime complex reacts very rapidly with EDTA while no reaction with the analogous nickel complex occurs. Thus it is possible to prepare quantitatively in solution $[Cu \, EDTA]^{-2}$ and $[Ni(PnAO)—H]^+$ and measure their color difference.

The design of such analytical methods requires a knowledge of reaction mechanisms and their relationship to reaction speeds.

The ability to place a metal in the gaseous state has value for purposes of separation, purification, and identification. Often this can be accomplished through coordination, for many types of volatile metal complexes are known. Three of the most useful types are the carbonyls, the acetylacetonates, and the cyclopentadienyl compounds. Pure nickel can be obtained by the fractional distillation of $Ni(CO)_4$, followed by thermal decomposition. Separations by gas chromatography at high temperatures can be accomplished with transition metal acetylacetonates of the formula $[M(acac)_3]^0$. Even some of the tetravalent metals can be made to form volatile complexes, such as $[Zn(acac)_4]^0$. A recently synthesized group of complexes having remarkable thermal stability are those patterned after ferrocene, $(C_5H_5)_2Fe$. A large number of such compounds have been prepared with, for example, Ni, V, Co, Cr. They are usually low-melting solids, many of which can be volatilized under vacuum. Their high stability, solubility in organic solvents, and ease of preparation may make them extremely valuable in the laboratory and in industry.

Few processes are as efficient or as easily and cheaply carried out under industrial conditions as is multiple solvent extraction. In metal ion extraction, purification, or separation, this often calls for metal complexes which are soluble in water-immiscible organic solvents. Many metal ions form inner complexes with dithizone which are extremely soluble in chloroform. Certain metals such as Ce^{+4} and Au^{+3} are easily extracted into ether from strong nitric acid solutions, which gives a convenient method of separating these ions from those of other metals.

Coordinating agents are widely used in industry to prevent metal ions from exhibiting their normal reaction properties. In the laboratory such practices as adding CN^- to mixtures of Cu^{+2} and Cd^{+2} to prevent the coprecipitation of CuS with CdS are well known. Softening hard water by the addition of EDTA or polyphosphates has tremendous industrial importance. Prevention of precipitate formation of trace metals in a variety of products by the use of chelating agents of the EDTA type is an accomplishment of recent development.

Biochemical Reactions

The role of metal complexes in biochemistry is extremely large, complicated, and of great importance. The action of many enzymes is dependent on coordinated metal ions incorporated in their structures. In addition, numerous non-enzymic reactions are catalyzed by metal ions, and they appear to function in much the same way as the enzyme, but usually the catalytic activity of the simple metal ion is below that of the natural enzyme.

The influence of coordinated metal ions in biological systems has been shown for the following types of changes: (1) bond cleavage reactions, (2) exchange reactions, and (3) oxidation-reduction reactions.

As an example of the first type we will use the decarboxylation of ketoacids. The conversion of oxaloacetic acid to pyruvic acid (6-2) is catalyzed by metal-containing decarboxylases. This reaction takes place under the influence of

$$\underset{\text{Oxaloacetic acid}}{HOOC-\overset{\beta}{C}H_2-\overset{\alpha}{\underset{\underset{O}{\|}}{C}}-COOH} \rightarrow \underset{\text{Pyruvic acid}}{CH_3\underset{\underset{O}{\|}}{C}-COOH} + CO_2 \qquad (6\text{-}2)$$

metal ions, even in the absence of enzyme protein. Esterification of the α-carboxyl group of oxaloacetic acid prevents the metal ion catalysis, suggesting a chelated intermediate involving the α-carboxyl group. The mechanism proposed is given in 6-3. A similar situation exists in the Fe^{+3} catalysis of

$$HOOC-CH_2-\underset{\underset{M^{+2}}{\overset{\cdots}{\underset{O^-}{|}}}}{\underset{\overset{\|}{O}}{C}}-C=O \xrightarrow{-CO_2} CH_3-\underset{\underset{M^{+2}}{\overset{\cdots}{\underset{O^-}{|}}}}{\underset{\overset{\|}{O}}{C}}-C=O \xrightarrow{H^+}$$

$$CH_3-\underset{\underset{O}{\|}}{C}-COOH + M^{+2} \qquad (6\text{-}3)$$

the decarboxylation of dimethyloxaloacetic acid. In this case it was shown that α-carboxyl, but not β-carboxyl, esterification prevents complex formation, thus favoring the same mechanism (6-3). A good correlation exists between the complex stability of the metal ions and their catalytic efficiency. The order of increasing stability and increasing catalytic properties is $Ca^{+2} < Mg^{+2} < Zn^{+2} < Fe^{+2} < Cu^{+2} < Fe^{+3} < Al^{+3}$. The influence of the protein in the enzyme seems to be to alter the electronic structure of the metal ion to give the optimum catalytic ability, and also to render the enzyme specific for one organic molecule. Such specificity is usually not found with simple metal ions.

The exchange of functional groups can be described in terms of the transamination reaction whose natural occurrence has been shown in the reaction of glutamic acid with pyruvic acid (6-4). This reaction is catalyzed by trans-

$$\underset{\text{Glutamic acid}}{HOOC\text{—}CH_2CH_2\underset{\underset{NH_2}{|}}{CH}\text{—}COOH} \quad + \quad \underset{\text{Pyruvic acid}}{CH_3\underset{\underset{O}{\|}}{C}\text{—}COOH} \quad \rightarrow$$

$$\underset{\alpha\text{-Ketoglutaric acid}}{HOOC\text{—}CH_2CH_2\underset{\underset{O}{\|}}{C}\text{—}COOH} \quad + \quad \underset{\text{Alanine}}{CH_3\text{—}\underset{\underset{NH_2}{|}}{CH}\text{—}COOH} \quad (6\text{-}4)$$

aminase enzymes and by various metal ions (Cu^{+2}, Fe^{+2}, Al^{+3}). It has been postulated that the reaction proceeds through a Schiff's base intermediate (6-5) utilizing a coenzyme, pyridoxal (vitamin B_6). The formation of metal–Schiff's base complexes has been established, and the mechanism given may also apply to the enzymic reaction.

Oxidation of the sulfhydryl group of cysteine is important in many biological systems. These reactions probably involve cysteine molecules associated with metal-ion-

$$M^{+2} + R-\underset{\underset{\text{COOH}}{|}}{CHNH_2} + \underset{\underset{\text{OH}}{|}}{O=CH-R'} \rightarrow$$

Glutamic acid

$$\underset{\underset{O}{\overset{|}{\underset{\|}{O=C}}}}{R-CH-N=CH}\diagdown_{\substack{R' \\ M-O}} \rightarrow \underset{\underset{O}{\overset{|}{\underset{\|}{O=C}}}}{R-C=N-CH_2}\diagdown_{\substack{R' \\ M-O}} \rightarrow$$

$$\underset{\underset{O}{\|}}{R-C-COOH} + \underset{\underset{OH}{|}}{NH_2CH_2-R'}$$

α-Ketoglutaric acid

$$R = HOOC-CH_2-CH_2-$$

$$R' = \text{—} \underset{\underset{CH_3}{}}{\bigcirc}_N$$

+ pyruvic acid

Alanine + Pyridoxal   (6-5)

containing proteins in natural systems. Although pure cysteine reacts very slowly with oxygen, the presence of Fe^{+2} causes oxygen uptake, which is accompanied by appearance of a deep purple color. On standing this color fades, owing to the reduction of the Fe^{+3} complex to the Fe^{+2} ion, but is regenerated upon addition of O_2, and the process continues until all of the cysteine is oxidized to cystine. The overall reaction may be viewed as occurring in three steps (6-6).

$$Fe^{+2} + 3\,HSCH_2CH(NH_2)COOH \xrightarrow{-6H^+} [Fe^{+2}(cysteine)_3]^{-4}$$

Cysteine

$$\Big\downarrow O_2$$

(6-6)

$$\begin{array}{c} Fe^{+2} \\ + \\ \text{Cysteine} \end{array} + \underset{\text{Cystine}}{\underset{|}{\overset{SCH_2CH(NH_2)COOH}{\overset{|}{SCH_2CH(NH_2)COOH}}}} \longleftarrow [Fe^{+3}(cysteine)_3]^{-3}$$

Violet color

SELECTED READINGS

Bailar, J. C., Jr., and D. Busch, "Chemistry of Coordination Compounds," Reinhold, New York, 1956.

Basolo, F., and R. G. Pearson, "Mechanisms of Inorganic Reactions," Wiley, New York, 1958.

Busch, D. H., ed., "Reactions of Coordinated Ligands," *Advances in Chemistry Series*, 37, American Chemical Society, Washington, D. C., 1963.

Cotton, F. A., and G. Wilkinson, "Advanced Inorganic Chemistry," Interscience, New York, 1962.

Edwards, J. O., "Inorganic Reaction Mechanisms," Benjamin, New York, 1964.

Emeléus, H. J., and A. G. Sharpe, eds., "Advances in Inorganic Chemistry and Radiochemistry," Academic, New York, 1959——.

"Mechanisms of Redox Reactions of Simple Chemistry," by H. Taube, ch. 1 of vol. I (1959).

"Mechanisms of Substitution Reactions of Metal Complexes," by F. Basolo and R. G. Pearson, ch. 1 of vol. III (1961).

Heslop, R. B., and P. L. Robinson, "Inorganic Chemistry," Elsevier, Amsterdam, 1960.

Ingraham, L. L., "Biochemical Mechanisms," Wiley, New York, 1962.

Kleinberg, J., W. J. Argersinger, Jr., and E. Griswold, "Inorganic Chemistry," Heath, Boston, 1960.

Lewis, J., and R. G. Wilkins, eds., "Modern Coordination Chemistry," Interscience, New York, 1960.

Pauling, L., "The Nature of the Chemical Bond," 3rd ed., Cornell Univ. Press, Ithaca, N. Y., 1960.

Selwood, P. W., "Magnetochemistry," 2nd ed., Interscience, New York, 1956.

INDEX

Absorption, visible and ultraviolet, 11
Acid-base properties, 93
Acid dissociation constants of metal ions, 94 (table)
Activated state, 55
Activation energy, 63
Activity coefficient, 28
Amineoxime complexes, 12, 112
Ammonia, rates of exchange with hexammines, 103
Analysis for metals, 112, 113
Applications of coordination theory, 110
Arrhenius equation, 63
Biochemical reactions, 115
Bjerrum method of determining formation constants, 32
Calorimeter, 51
Chelate, definition, 17–18
Chelate effect, 26, 44, 45
Chlorophyll, 8
cis-trans isomerization, 87
cis-trans isomers, chemical properties, 85
cis-trans ratio, 86
Complexes of NO_2^-, 9, 108, 111
Conductivity, 10
Configurations of metal ions, 69
Coordination compound(s), definition, 3, 4
history, 1–3
Coordination number, 3, 16, 17
changes, 45
Crystal field stabilization energy (CFSE), 73

Crystal field theory, 66, 71
Cysteine–cystine, 117
Degenerate orbitals, 72
Deuterium exchange, 100
Dimethylglyoxime, 6, 48, 107
Displacement, 97
Donor atoms, 19, 40
Electroplating, 110
Energy levels, octahedral state, 73
tetrahedral and planar states, 75
Enthalpy change, definition, 27
Entropy change, 27, 52–53
Ethylenediaminetetraacetic acid, 6, 9, 48
Ferrocene, 81
Formation constant(s), and basicity of ligand, 41, 42
definition, 27
measurement, 29–38
Formulas, 15
Geometrical isomers, octahedral, 83
planar, 82
α-Glycols, reaction with $B(OH)_3$, 11
Gold: $AuCl_4^- - Cl^-$ exchange rates, 101
Heats of reaction, 49–52
Hemin, 8
High spin, 76
Hybridization, 67
Hydration number of Cr^{+3}, 102
Hydrogenation, 106
"Inner" and "outer" sphere complexes, 69
Intermolecular mechanism, 89
Intramolecular mechanism, 89

Ion exchange, 14, 34
Isomerization, *cis-trans*, 87
    racemization, 88
Isotopic dilution, 59
Isotopic exchange, mechanisms, 59, 100
Job's method, 32–33
Kinetics, 54–65
Kinetic stability, 10
Lewis, G. N., 3
Ligand(s), 16 (table)
    effects on stability, 39
    mono- and multidentate, 17
Ligand exchange, 97
Ligand field stabilization energy (LFSE), 47
Ligand splitting ability, 77
Low spin, 76
Mechanisms of reaction, 107
Metal ion, effects on stability, 46
Monodentate, definition, 17
Multidentate, definition, 17
Naming, 19–22
Nickel: $[Ni(CN)_4]^{-4}$, 92
    $[Ni(CN)_3]^{-2}$, 92
Nitrito-nitro rearrangement of cobalt(III) ammines, 108
Nomenclature, early, 2
    rules, 19–22
Octahedral substitution, mechanism, 97
Optical activity, 14
Optical isomers, octahedral, 84
    tetrahedral, 83
Orbital hybridization, 68
Oxidation state, bonding, 79
    stabilization, 90
Pauling, Linus, 3
Planar substitution, mechanism, 99

Racemization, 88
Rate constant, definition, 57
Rate measurement, 55–60
Reaction mechanisms, 56, 64, 65, 87, 88, 97, 99, 100, 101, 103
Reactions of coordinated ligands, 103
Ring size, 45
Separation of isomers, 84
Silver: $[Ag(dipy)_2]^{+2}$ and $[Ag(py)_4]^{+2}$, 92
Softening of hard water, 114
Solubility, 14
    of AgI and AgCl, 9–10
Stability constants, ligand effects, 39–46
    metal ion effects, 46–48
    solvent effects, 48
Standard free energy change, definition, 27
Stepwise formation, 26
Steric effects, 42, 43, 44
Stereoisomerism, coordination, 24
    geometrical, 22
    ionization, 23
    linkage, 24
    ligand, 24
    optical, 22
Titration curve, 13
Transamination, 116
Uses of coordination compounds, 6, 7
Valence bond theory, 66
Visible and ultraviolet absorption, 11
Vitamin B_{12}, 8
Voltage measurements, 37
Werner, Alfred, 2